Living a Holistic Lifestyle

Beginners Guide to a Healthy Body, Mind, and Soul

Michelle Stern

D1502861

Table of Contents

INTRODUCTION **7**

CHAPTER 1

Living a Holistic Lifestyle **10**

CHAPTER 2

Physical Health is the Foundation of a Holistic Lifestyle **13**

CHAPTER 3

Your Holistic Lifestyle Starts With Healthy Eating **16**

CHAPTER 4

How to Know if You Are Buying Organic Food **25**

CHAPTER 5

Why Are Herbs Important For Good Health? **28**

CHAPTER 6

Which Types of Exercise Should You Do? **36**

CHAPTER 7

Why Connecting to Nature is Crucial **40**

CHAPTER 8

How Your Environment Affects Your Health **45**

CHAPTER 9

Natural Healing Modalities **52**

CHAPTER 10

Our Five Daily Needs **57**

CHAPTER 11

How Mental and Emotional Health Affect the Body **67**

CHAPTER 12

Why is Personal Development Important? **79**

CHAPTER 13

Spiritual Health; Evolution of Your Soul **89**

CHAPTER 14

Why a Life Purpose is Necessary **99**

CHAPTER 15

Why Connecting to the Universe Is Important **103**

Conclusion **108**

About the Author **111**

INTRODUCTION

Never has our society been in such desperate need of a healthcare overhaul as right now. More and more people are developing chronic illnesses and cancer. We can't point the finger at any one factor; the healthcare system itself, toxins in our environment, food, air, and water, unhealthy habits almost all of us have, etc. People are overweight, unhealthy, depressed, filled with anxiety, disconnected from nature and a higher power, and as a result, we are not the best version of ourselves we can be. We are not living to our full potential. And worse of all, we don't believe we can change it.

When it comes to making changes, there are a few things that must happen first. The average person isn't just going to wake up on a random day and change their life. First, they must feel pain or discomfort. And it has to be a lot of it. Nobody makes a change unless the pain of staying the same becomes worse than the pain of changing.

Furthermore, we can't know for sure what we will gain from changing, but we do know for sure what we will lose from staying the same. Staying safe and comfortable in a moderate amount of pain is better than taking a risk, getting uncomfortable, and maybe not even getting a result.

So, once the pain becomes unbearable, the other side starts to look better and better. Finally, the person decides to make the change. The emotional pain caused a chain reaction, and something clicked mentally, which then results in physical action.

But many times, the change doesn't stick. It's too hard--it's too uncomfortable--it will take too long, etc. This is where you must become your own cheerleader, your own coach, your own motivational speaker. You must tell yourself that yes, it is hard, but it will be worth it. Yes, it is uncomfortable, but that won't last long. Yes, it will take a long time, but the time is going to pass anyway, so you have to ask yourself if you would rather arrive in the future a different person or the same person. You have to ask yourself if you genuinely want to change or if you want more pain and suffering before you can want it enough.

Have you had enough of getting put on medications, and more medications to cover up the side effects of those medications? Have you had enough of wandering aimlessly through life with no goals other than to make it through another day at your job (which you hate)? Have you had enough of feeling like you are disconnected to the greater whole? Have you had enough of anxiety and depression? Have you had enough of running and getting nowhere like a mouse in the wheel? Have you had enough of feeling numb, complacent, and apathetic?

A holistic lifestyle is not just about physical health; it's also about mental, emotional, and spiritual health. You are a whole person, so why not treat yourself as such? Give all of yourself the love, respect, and attention you deserve. You can't get very far if one part of you is dragging the other parts down.

This book is an introduction for people who don't know much about holistic health at all or know some but want to know more. It is for those who feel overwhelmed by how to change their lifestyle when there is so much to learn and do that you don't know where to start. This book is for you if you want to expand your knowledge about holistic health and decide what aspects to integrate into your life. This book is also for you if you love learning about holistic health already but just need more guidance to turn it into a lifestyle. You want to live it, not just read about it!

Since you purchased this book, you have at least a passing interest in holistic health. It is ok if you don't fully understand what it means. It is ok if you only want to learn the basics and go on your way. I don't judge your level of commitment. I only want the opportunity to change your life for the better.

Don't let the negative thoughts convince you that you can't do this. It all starts with the mind. You have to believe you can change your life, and you will succeed if you get out of your own way.

My main goal is to help you grow and evolve your body, mind, and soul into the best version they can be! And with nature on our side, it's practically guaranteed we will succeed!

CHAPTER 1

Living a Holistic Lifestyle

What is a holistic lifestyle, and what's in it for you?

Let's start with the word "holistic," which means whole. When it comes to health, every aspect of ourselves needs attention to reach optimal health. The whole person includes the body, mind, and soul, or spirit.

If your body is failing, your mind and soul will suffer as well. And likewise, your mind and spirit can affect your body. So, making sure all systems are operating correctly is vital to your overall health and well-being. Conventional healthcare doesn't often address your mind or your spirit, and if it does, it usually just covers the symptoms with a pill and hopes you come out okay with that. Living a holistic lifestyle is taking control of your own health, and giving the body, mind, and soul what they need, aligning back to nature, and staying in balance.

The body. Physical health could be considered the most fundamental building block of holistic health. Eating whole foods, preferably organic, is the cornerstone to optimal health. Daily movement and exercise, sunlight, and sleep are also crucial to keeping the body in prime shape. And of course, it is wise to find natural remedies and healing modalities before resorting to pharmaceutical drugs and surgery. The body is a natural thing, and we should strive to keep it that way.

The mind. Emotional and mental health is just as important as physical health. Negative thoughts, stress, and trauma have horrible effects on the body that often can't be seen until it is too late. It is also essential to expand your mind and consciousness or awareness. We live in a great big world, don't limit your world to your living room and whatever the TV is shoving in your face. Become a well-rounded person by traveling, exercising your brain, and soaking up as much knowledge as you can. Mental health also includes cutting toxic relationships out of your life and raising your vibration so you attract more mentally healthy people.

The soul. Many people disregard this or don't think about it. But it is essential if you are trying to achieve a holistically optimized life. Most people are not in touch with their soul. Most people simply exist; they don't thrive! Personal development and self-reflection are essential for finding your life purpose. Exploring spirituality (which may or may not include a religion) also enhances your health.

Truly living holistically is a lifestyle. It means more than just eating fruits and vegetables, more than just reading a book here and there about spiritual things. It's about aligning yourself with nature and the universe and committing to evolve your body, mind, and soul to a state of wholeness we were meant to enjoy.

You may have already tried to make changes in your life with no success. You have probably encountered obstacles that made you feel like giving up. Living a truly holistic lifestyle takes some work. But it is fun work, and it certainly helps when you have an idea of the direction to take and have the information you need to motivate you.

Maybe you consider the topic of holistic health to be more of a hobby; turning a hobby into a lifestyle only takes repetition and consistency. I really like the quote, "We are what we repeatedly do."; I see conflicting citations on who actually said this, but it sums up how I feel about turning a passing interest into a lifestyle.

It all comes down to routine. Don't worry; routine doesn't have to mean boring! The self-care routines that make up a holistic lifestyle bring calm and inner peace that cannot be experienced by doing them sporadically. Just like meditation and yoga, the benefits take a few weeks to kick in. But once they do, you will want them to be routine!

So, what is the best way to achieve holistic health? If you guessed living in harmony with nature, you are right! We must play by nature's rules if we are to thrive. Nature knows what it's doing, and I trust something that has been in business since the beginning of time!

While a typical office visit often consists of finding a drug to match a disease, alternative medicine addresses the underlying causes to maximize overall well-being.

In essence, alternative medicine aims to heal you naturally, from the inside out, while modern medicine acts as a band-aid, hoping that masking the symptoms on the outside will magically fix the original problem on the inside. As you are probably figuring out by now, it does not work that way.

I don't think I need to remind you of all the horrible side effects of pharmaceutical drugs; most of them are worse than the symptom they are treating! Then you need to go back to the doctor to get another pill for those side effects! It's madness. And a holistic lifestyle can put a stop to that, or at least drastically reduce the madness.

Humans are made of the same elements that make up animals, trees, flowers, and rocks. To me, it makes more sense to drink herbal tea for an ailment than to run to the doctor to get prescribed pills for the rest of your life.

CHAPTER 2

Physical Health is the Foundation of a Holistic Lifestyle

Your well-being should be a priority in your life, yet so many of us place health too low on our priority list. Health seems to be something that's often taken for granted. We feel invincible until it fails us. This is clearly the wrong attitude.

If you take preventative action, you'll not only feel better, but your body will thank you by adding years onto your life! Years not in a nursing home but leading an active life.

I can't stress enough how important physical health is to holistic health. It is the foundation of everything else. You wouldn't build a house without making sure the foundation was laid correctly. The same applies to your body. This may seem like common sense to you, but it is so important to get right.

You might be familiar with Maslow's hierarchy of needs. If you are not, here is a diagram to help you visualize which levels of human development must come before other levels can be reached.

Maslow's hierarchy of needs (1943)

As you can see, when looking at the bottom level, all humans need food, water, shelter, air, and warmth to survive. Physical health falls within this first category.

Physical health and mental health are no doubt intricately tied, so one could argue that you should get your mind right before getting your body right. For the sake of simplicity and keeping your journey smoother, we'll start with physical health.

Excellent physical health of the body can be achieved when all four of these factors are optimal;

- healthy diet/proper nutrition
- daily habits (exercise, sleep, etc.)
- healing naturally
- environment

While there are hundreds of diets out there, you could give yourself a mind-boggling headache researching all of them. I have been there, and what I have learned from all my years of trying to figure out the best lifestyle for optimum health is simply this; the more in harmony with nature your lifestyle is, the healthier you will be.

Forget fad diets, forget straining yourself at the gym seven days a week, forget a cupboard full of artificial supplements. Humans are simple creatures who came from nature. The answer to most health problems lies in a natural, simple lifestyle.

Humans would do well to follow our Earthly counterparts' lead; animals! In the wild, animals don't die of cancer or get diabetes.

When humans domesticated animals as our pets and gave them man-made feed-grade pellets, we unwittingly brought them along for the ride on the disease train. That is further proof that humans should wake up and learn what is really in our food, and subsequently make healthier choices.

CHAPTER 3

Your Holistic Lifestyle Starts With Healthy Eating

This is where your journey begins! Healthy eating is the most fundamental part of optimal physical health.

It's one thing to understand how important eating healthy is. It's quite another to be ready to commit, or at least be eager to learn.

If you do nothing else, eating the right foods (and less of the wrong ones) is a good start. Changing your entire lifestyle to focus around health is extreme and not for everyone, but just mastering what you put into your body will have a profound effect.

When you eat poorly, you're doing a massive disservice to your body. Everything you eat either supports health or supports disease; the choice is up to you.

Healthy eating is the most straightforward part of living a holistic lifestyle. There are only a few questions to ask yourself when wondering what is healthy to eat.

- Is it a whole food?
- Has it been heavily processed?
- Was it grown using antibiotics or pesticides?
- Are there any harmful chemicals added?

To take the guesswork out of this, you can consider yourself relatively safe if you aim to buy organic. If you don't want to spend your whole paycheck at Whole Foods, you can still eat pretty healthy by eating "whole foods." These are simply fruits, vegetables, nuts, seeds, whole grains, legumes, and beans.

As long as a food item didn't come into being in a factory mixed with chemicals and then processed until it was no longer recognizable, then you can consider yourself safe eating it. Ideally, we should all grow our own vegetables, as this is the only food group that all the diets agree you should eat in large quantities. And if you grow them all yourself, or at least a vast majority of them, then you will save a ton of money and be more inclined to eat healthy.

A primary rule of thumb is to cut back on sugar or even block it out entirely. Starches like white rice, bread, and pasta are also high on the list of foods we should avoid.

Here is a good list of healthy alternatives to the main foods that contain sugar and starch. This list was hard to narrow down, but they all show up on almost every top 10 healthiest food list, so while there are hundreds more, this is an excellent place to start!

- Berries (Blueberries and Raspberries especially)
- Sweet Potatoes
- Broccoli
- Oats (steel-cut oatmeal is much better than instant oatmeal)
- Leafy greens (spinach, kale, chard)
- Nuts (almonds, pecans, walnuts, and cashews are best)
- Avocados
- Beans
- Garlic
- Lemons
- Chia Seeds
- Quinoa
- Salmon (caught in the wild, not factory farmed)
- Lentils

When it comes to eating meat, there are three kinds of people. Vegetarians & vegans don't eat any meat, carnivores eat meat whenever they want, and then there are those torn in the middle who don't want to give up their favorite foods that include meat, but also don't overdo eating meat. Falling into this middle category isn't a bad thing, because there are ways you can get your meat without suffering the consequences (or at least not nearly as much).

Eating animal products affects humans negatively, especially if those animals were slaughtered in an inhumane way. The subject of humans eating animal meat will probably always be controversial. I have heard evidence that vegetarians are healthier, but I have also heard after some length of time, the body will show signs of needing protein.

Lean grass-fed beef eaten in moderation is best, as is eating free-roam chickens. Cage-free chickens are still not allowed to go outside, so that is a misleading term. Fish is good if it is wild-caught (as opposed to factory-farmed).

There are also completely meat-less alternatives out there to replace meat, chicken, and cheese. You can find these in mainstream grocery stores if you look hard, but places like Whole Foods, Natural Grocers, and Fresh Thyme have sections just for meat and dairy-free alternatives.

It is arguably much easier to eat right when you cook your own food. It's no surprise that home cooking is essential for healthy eating. We all know restaurant food is a big no-no, although there are some pretty good exceptions popping up in big cities.

But overall, you will do much better cooking at home; and by cooking, I don't mean throwing some pre-packaged junk in the microwave for a few minutes.

It's a pretty hard fact to face, but generally, most packaged food that comes in a box or a can has been showered in preservatives, anti-caking agents, and too much salt. There are a few exceptions, but you'd be better off cooking your own meals from scratch as much as possible.

I personally can barely stomach canned vegetables. Frozen is much better because there is no need for the massive amounts of salt like there is in canned foods.

Freezing the food also retains the nutrients much better. Sometimes I doubt if canned foods even have any nutrients left in them. Fresh is still the best. It does require more frequent trips to the store, but your body will thank you!

Design your diet for success. Just like with anything else, a good plan helps you achieve your desired results. Spending time designing your diet will pay off for you. Make a list of all the things you have in your fridge and cupboard. Research the nutritional information on these items.

Which ones are good and which ones aren't? Replace the bad food choices with healthier options, and then keep the healthy ones coming!

A lot of people ask about supplements. In all the research I have done and the education I have gotten, I still can't find a definite answer on whether or not supplements are good for you. To be sure, some are. Do we need them? That is probably a case by case situation.

I think what is more important is that if you buy supplements, buy the best quality ones. This is a lot like organic vs. conventional foods; you get what you pay for. There is a website called Consumer Lab worth checking out. They independently study supplements and give their ratings on which ones are the best.

A lot of the cheaper supplements have been found to include mostly filler. Do your research. Trust the companies that have the organic label and have a good reputation.

Supplements give good peace of mind, like insurance. However, it's easy to go overboard, so please try to get your vitamins and minerals from food rather than pills. Rarely are supplements superior to healthy eating.

If you do buy supplements, here is a quick guide for how to pick the right ones;

Low-Quality Ingredients

Carbonates
Oxides
Sulfates
Phosphates

High-Quality Ingredients

Ascorbates
Glycinates
Citrates
Malates
Tartrates
Succinates
Sebacates

Vitamin B-12

Buy with the ingredients METHYLcobalain or HYDROXOcobolamin
CYANOcobolamin, on the other hand, is not natural and doesn't get utilized by the body as well.

Vitamin C

Buy with L-Ascorbate, NOT D-Ascorbate. L is natural, D is not. L can be utilized by the body better.

Vitamin D

Buy D3, not D2. D2 is cheaper, therefore, more commonly used, however, D3 is so much more easily absorbed and utilized by the body.

If you don't want to pop manufactured pills every day, nature has given us the gift of herbs! I cannot say enough good things about herbs, and I also cannot stress how important they are to living a holistic lifestyle.

Herbs do so much for us physically, mentally, and emotionally! There are thousands of herbs out there with different constitutions, so there is an herb (or ten) for every ailment. Herbalism is such a vast field of study; it is beyond the scope of this book to dive in deep. But I do have a chapter just on herbs coming up later.

You might wonder, what is the healthiest thing you can drink? You guessed it; water! Nothing else even comes close. Of course, tea is the next best thing, but that kind of goes without saying since all tea is is water and herbs.

You've heard it before, we are made up of mostly water, so since we are what we drink, please don't drink the kool-aid! Or the soda! Or the alcohol!

About the only two non-water drinks that are ok in moderation are red wine and coffee, both of which do have a few health benefits as long as they are taken in moderation.

As for energy drinks like Monster and Red Bull, do not drink these. Basically, anything that includes sugar, chemicals (things you can't pronounce), and dyes (red #40, blue #2, yellow #6, etc.) stay far away from these!

This should be common sense, but somewhere along the line, these poisons became introduced into our food and drinks, and the rest is history. By reading labels and educating yourself on exactly what these things are and how to avoid them, you are well on your way to good health.

A word about milk; people are pretty divided on whether or not milk is good for us. Many people feel better after cutting dairy out of their diets. Some people do have a legit adverse reaction to milk, and others can drink it just fine.

My personal belief is this; human babies don't drink breast milk their whole lives, so why did it ever become a thing for adults to drink the milk of another species? It just seems to go against nature to me. It is not even taking into account the horrible treatment of cows and the industrialized chemical process of making that milk safe to drink.

If you are lactose intolerant, goats' milk is a better choice than cow's milk. It is easier for humans to digest due to its lower lactose levels, smaller fat molecules, and being naturally homogenized, lessening the need for processing.

If drinking any animal's milk sounds disgusting to you, there is always almond milk, rice milk, coconut milk, soy milk, flax milk, oat milk, and hemp milk.

You might be wondering; how can you eat healthy when you hate the taste of vegetables? Veggies seem to get the most hate out of all the foods out there. They taste like dirt; I get it. They're not as satisfying as a gooey bowl of macaroni and cheese, I hear you. This is why herbs and spices were given to us by nature (nature might not care if we like vegetables, but I like to think she does!)

Anything can be made palatable with a little time and effort to research recipes. Salt and pepper, for starters, are the most common way to season your food. You can add cheese to some vegetables (yes, there are healthy versions of cheese!)

And of course, there are somewhere around 100 different spices in the world, and just like variety is the spice of life, let spices give variety to your food! Healthy eating doesn't have to be flavorless!

Up until a few hundred years ago, the food humans ate was not processed and factory-farmed. Our ancestors ate off the land, living according to nature. Oh, what a price we pay today for convenience!

Humans have never been sicker. There are more diseases and kinds of cancer popping up almost weekly; it seems like. Doesn't it make you wish you could hop in a time machine and eat like they did a few thousand years ago?

Well, you can! Have you ever heard of a little thing called Ayurveda? It's actually the world's oldest health system, beginning in India a few thousand years ago. The word "Ayurveda" means the science of life.

It is a lifestyle system consisting of carefully chosen foods tailored to everyone's individual constitution, daily self-care rituals, and detoxing methods. When researching lifestyles that most closely worked in harmony with nature, Ayurveda is the clear winner.

Ayurveda states that everyone is born with a unique combination of doshas. Dosha is a Sanskrit word meaning "constitution." Each of the three doshas is made up of different aspects of the elements; Earth, Air, Fire, Water, and Space.

To keep it simple for now, every food, herb, and spice on the planet either pacifies or aggravates each dosha. So, according to Ayurveda, you will always be healthy if you eat the right foods for your dosha.

The system also advises that we eat the foods that are in season, as well as living in harmony with nature in other ways. It is such a vast system. It is the only lifestyle I have found that is based around total harmony with nature.

For more information on Ayurveda, I will provide a few suggestions for my favorite websites about Ayurveda. The first one is Banyan Botanicals. This site has a series of quizzes that are free to take so you can find out which dosha you are and receive individualized recommendations on how to live a lifestyle in accordance with your dosha. This site is extremely comprehensive, including how-do videos and products you can order.

Sahara Rose is the author of the best-selling book "Idiot's Guide to Ayurveda." I read this book, among many others, and found this to be the easiest to follow, written for the complete beginner, and highly recommended! Her website is called I Am Sahara Rose. She also has a course on Ayurveda, which I highly recommend!

CHAPTER 4

How to Know if You Are Buying Organic Food

Deciphering organic food labels is pretty simple. Here is a basic rundown of what to look for on the label;

- "100% Organic" means the food was made with 100% organic ingredients.
- "Organic" means the food was made with at least 95% organic ingredients.
- "Made With Organic Ingredients" means the food was made with at least 70% organic ingredients.
- The USDA Organic Seal (shown here) is what you want to see to be sure the food is organic.

For produce sold loose, not in packaging, check the price sticker;

- A five-digit number that starts with a nine means the produce **is** organic.
- A four-digit number means the produce is **not** organic.

A scary fact about buying organic produce in a grocery store is that it most likely was shipped there across the country or at least a few hundred miles away. Fruit is often picked before it is ripe, sprayed with wax to preserve it, and stored for weeks or even months!

Hands down, the healthiest way to get organic food is to grow it yourself. Gardening is one of the best things you can do for your health. Aside from enjoying healthy food right outside your door, you also get the benefit of digging in the Earth, which is all kinds of good for you! If you don't have your own yard, don't fret! There are plenty of other options.

If you really want to do your own gardening but have no yard, you have a few options. Many things can be grown in a container on your porch, balcony, or windowsill. Any room that gets sun would work. Herbs are especially easy and suitable to grow in small containers.

You could also join a community garden. You pay a small monthly fee (usually paid for one growing season at a time), and you get your own little plot. The downside to this is you must go there, lugging all your gardening tools with you.

The next best option is to go to a farmer's market. Most cities and towns have a farmer's market. Another option is to join a CSA, which stands for Community Supported Agriculture. There are CSA's everywhere, and they all have different prices and paying options. Some of them even deliver to your house.

Supporting your local farmers is a great way to eat healthy, save money, and build community. We vote with our dollars, and the more people that buy organic food, the cheaper it will get overall.

An excellent website for finding farmers markets and CSA's is called Local Harvest.

Most grocery stores these days have a separate organic section, and there are also many local co-ops to shop at, as well as some chain health stores such as Whole Foods and Natural Grocers. These are all more spendy options, but at least organic food is readily available.

CHAPTER 5

Why Are Herbs Important For Good Health?

Herbs have medicinal properties, and they grow in nature, so it makes sense to use herbs in your diet. Many pharmaceutical drugs are derived from plants; however, they extract only parts of the plant, so you are not getting the plant as a whole as nature intended. Why would you choose a man-made pill over something that grows on the Earth for that purpose?

There is an herb for every ailment. However, herbs shine best when used for prevention purposes. They usually have a more subtle effect, a more slow-building effect. This is why most herbs aren't useful for emergencies, although there are a few that are. Basically, though, herbs are one of the best natural ways to prevent illness and get chronic diseases under control.

Herbs are either tonic or nutritive. **Tonic herbs** help the body assimilate nutrients. **Nutritive herbs** provide mineral and vitamins in a way that the body can easily assimilate them.

There are two ways to use herbs. Generally, an herb is either used in **cooking** (along with spices) or used **medicinally** either in the prevention of disease or to treat an illness. Many herbs can be used for both. Some work better to eat, and some work better to drink in some form. First, I will cover medicinal herbs.

If you grow your own herbs at home, it will be so much more convenient to prepare them. They don't take up a lot of space if you must grow them indoors. Here is a basic overview of the main methods of using herbs;

Tea
1-2 TBS dried herbs
1-2 C boiling water

Let steep until it cools off enough to drink
Best for daily use of herbs for general health

Infusion
1 OZ. dried herbs
1 QT. boiling water

Let sit in a mason jar, covered, for many hours, preferably overnight
Best for daily herbs for general health, and preventative and maintenance purposes. Best for herbs that have highly volatile oils. Produces stronger flavor & extracts more of the constituents of the herbs.

Decoction
1 TB dried herbs (or 2 TB fresh herbs) for each cup of water

Use cold water to start
Place on heat
Boil, then simmer, covered, for up to 45 minutes.
Best for roots, barks, berries, and seeds of the plant.

Syrup
1 part already prepared decoction to 1 part honey (if this is too sweet, use more decoction, less honey)

Simmer over low heat until honey is dissolved (do **not** use high heat as this will destroy the beneficial properties of the honey!)
Let cool before bottling in a glass container. Store in the fridge.
Stays good for a few months. Best for medicinal uses (cough syrup,

immunity syrup). Elderberry syrup is the most common, used for colds and flus.

Elixir
No heat needed.
Fill glass jar 1/2 full of dried herbs, full if using fresh herbs.
Fill halfway with brandy, the rest of the way with honey. Stir well.
Cover, store for six weeks in a cool, dry place. Stir a few times a week.
After six weeks, strain out the herbs.
Best for medicinal uses.

Tincture
Fill herbs in glass container no more than 3/4 full (more if using fresh, less if using dried)
Fill container to the top with alcohol, most commonly vodka.
Use a plastic lid, or if using metal lid, put parchment paper on top of the herbs to keep the lid from corrosion.
Shake daily and make sure alcohol is still covering herbs. If not, add more alcohol.
After 6-8 weeks, strain herbs and store in a dark-colored glass container.
Best for medicinal uses.

Poultice
Used topically directly on the skin or through a thin mesh.
If using fresh herbs, crush finely. If using dry, mix with a little water to form a paste.
Use cold water (if necessary) for inflammation, hot water (if necessary) for increasing circulation.
Spread mashed herbs onto skin and wrap with a bandage. Or wrap herbs in muslin or gauze and secure onto the skin.
Best for skin irritations or localized pain.

There are many websites and books out there to dive deep into the world of herbalism, so for the sake of simplicity, I will just cover the basics here.

In general, when looking for an herb for a specific ailment, you want to choose an herb according to its properties.

Alterative
Normalizes the body, purifies the blood
Best for infections, cancer
Examples; Echinacea, Dandelion Root, Red Clover, Alfalfa, Calendula Flower, Ginseng, Licorice, Raspberry Leaf

Analgesic
Relieves pain
Examples; Chamomile, Lemongrass, Skullcap, Turmeric, Ginger, and Valerian.

Antacids
Neutralizes acid in the stomach.
Examples; Dandelion Root, Slippery Elm Bark

Antispasmodics
Relieves muscle cramping
Examples; Cayenne Pepper, Chamomile, Skullcap, Lavender, Lemon Balm, Mullein Leaf, Nettle Leaf, Valerian

Astringents/Anti-Inflammatory
Constricts the tissues
Best for hemorrhoids and wound healing.
Examples; Aloe Vera, Calendula, Cayenne Pepper, Cinnamon, Dandelion Root, Mullein Leaf, Peppermint, Raspberry Leaf, Rosehips

Carminatives
Relieves intestinal pain and gas
Best for digestive issues
Examples; Astragalus, Ginger, Chamomile, Cinnamon, Cloves, Ginseng, Lemon Balm, Lemongrass, Valerian, Lavender

Demulcents
Soothes inflames tissues.
Best for digestive issues, sinus problems

Examples; Burdock, Ginseng, Marshmallow Root, Mullein Leaf, Slippery Elm Bark, Milk Thistle, Licorice, Oat Straw

Diuretics
Encourages urine flow.
Best for water retention, kidney stones, urinary infections
Examples; Astragalus, Elder Berries, Marshmallow, Nettle Leaf, Burdock, Dandelion, Oat Straw, Red Clover, Hawthorn Berry

Emollients
Soothes and softens the skin
Examples; Aloe Vera, Marshmallow Root, Slippery Elm Bark

Expectorants
Expels excess mucus
Examples; Mullein, Ginseng, Lemongrass, Licorice, Nettle Leaf, Slippery Elm Bark, Red Clover

Laxatives
Stimulate bowel movements
Examples Aloe Vera, Buckthorn, Slippery Elm, Marshmallow Root, Chamomile, Dandelion

Nervines
Calm the nerves
Examples; Chamomile, Hops, Passionflower, Lemon Balm, Skullcap, Valerian, Skullcap

Stimulants
Stimulate the nervous system, increase energy
Examples; Ginkgo Biloba, Cayenne Pepper, Cinnamon, Ginseng, Ginger, Ginkgo Biloba, Peppermint, Astragalus

Tonics
General invigoration for the whole body
Examples; Burdock, Dandelion Root, Ginseng, Hawthorn Berry, Alfalfa, Milk Thistle

You can grow your own herbs, you can harvest them from the wild, or you can order them online. The ones you get online are, of course, dried, but sometimes they are your only option, especially in the wintertime. If you order them online, I highly recommend this site, Mountain Rose Herbs. My herbs always come pretty quickly, usually within five business days. They are one of the most recommended companies to get herbs from.

Herbs, and their sister, spices, are probably as important to cooking as the food itself. Many people don't realize the health benefits as well as the amazing flavors that herbs and spices provide. You might be guilty of this, just cooking food by itself, plopping it on the table, and instinctively reaching for the salt and pepper and calling it done. If you use herbs and spices in your cooking, your need for excess salt will diminish.

Basil
Have you ever bought dried basil only to find it didn't smell or taste like much of anything? That is because basil has aromatic oils that dissipate when the herb is dried. Fresh basil is just about one of the most fragrant and potent herbs out there. So always get fresh if you can! Basil is best with any type of Italian food, pizza, pasta, spaghetti, etc. It is best added last to keep the flavor strong. Basil covers a broad base when it comes to health. It is good for indigestion, fever, colds and flu, nausea, constipation, nervous disorders, muscle cramps, and kidney/urinary disorders.

Cayenne Pepper
The incredible thing about cayenne pepper is its ability to stop bleeding. It can actually be used directly on wounds and taken internally to prevent heart attacks. It is most commonly used in Mexican food or anything where you want a lot of kick!

Cilantro
Either you love cilantro, or you think it tastes like soap. There is actually a DNA-related reason for this, but if you love cilantro, you're in luck! It is an excellent source of antioxidants, phytochemicals, and Vitamin A. Cilantro is the same plant as coriander, which makes up the seeds. Cilantro is a must for Mexican

cooking, being one of the main ingredients in salsa. It also goes really well with rice and lime juice and is used extensively in Indian cuisine. Like basil, cilantro is delicate, so don't add this to cooked food until it is done.

Cinnamon
Cinnamon is warming, so it is good to drink as a tea as well as balancing out cold foods like fruits and desserts. It is useful to treat diarrhea, muscle cramps, indigestion, and gas.

Cumin
Cumin is used around most of the world, mostly in dishes like hummus, chutneys, lentils, chili, beans, and chicken. It is useful for eliminating and preventing gas, as well as being good for the heart.

Fennel
Fennel is actually a vegetable, with stalks that resemble celery. But the seeds are what are used as spices. They are a powerhouse of nutrients, minerals, antioxidants, and fiber. It is good for indigestion and relieving gas. Fennel seeds go well in breads, soups, meat, poultry, and sauces. You can also chew the seeds after a meal to help digestion and improve breath.

Garlic and Onion
Garlic has a wide range of health benefits, notably, it's potent anti-bacterial properties, making it a great choice to fight colds and flu. It is excellent for immune system health and heart health. It is used most commonly in Italian cooking. Onions are in the same family, and they are also very widely used in cooking to enhance the flavor or sauces, meats, stews, and soups.

Ginger
Ginger is one of the best spices for digestive issues. It is also good for the circulation. It is excellent for colds, especially when used with honey and lemon. Ginger is a pretty strong flavor, and spicy, so it might take some getting used to if you aren't already familiar with its taste. It is commonly drunk as a tea and also used to flavor fish, chicken, and many Asian foods.

Oregano
Oregano is used around the world, most commonly in Italian cooking. It is rich in antioxidants and has potent antibacterial and anti-inflammatory properties. Marjoram is related to oregano but has a milder, sweeter flavor.

Parsley
Parsley looks a lot like cilantro but has a more mild flavor. It can be used on most foods, from vegetables to soups to fish to rice. It is very rich in Vitamin C. It is an antioxidant, and also protects against cancer and heart disease.

Rosemary
Rosemary is good for headaches, indigestion, nausea, gas, and fever. It is overall good for the nervous system as well. Rosemary is excellent on bread, potatoes, and chicken. It holds up well so it can be cooked for the duration of the cooking time.

Sage
Along with rosemary and thyme, sage has many medicinal uses, including treating headaches, night sweats, diarrhea, and colds and flus. Sage is most commonly used to season wild game. It can also be drunk as a tea. In ancient times, it was thought to promote wisdom, which is probably where the term "wise old sage" comes from!

Thyme
Thyme has a wide variety of uses, including treating intestinal worms, bronchial problems, and diarrhea. It is most commonly used in Italian cooking. Like rosemary, thyme can withstand long cooking times.

Turmeric
Turmeric is widely known as the pungent yellow spice that is really good for you. More specifically, it contains curcumin, which is the active ingredient that gives it it's antioxidant and anti-inflammatory powers. However, it has been proven if you take curcumin as a supplement along with black pepper, you will get much better absorption. It is most commonly used in curries and Indian foods.

CHAPTER 6

Which Types of Exercise Should You Do?

There are a few myths out there about exercise. Do you feel like to stay healthy, you have to hit the gym every day, or that you must live by the "no pain no gain" rule? Do you feel like if you didn't break a sweat, it wasn't a real workout? Think again!

I come bearing good news! None of those things are necessary! In fact, the amount of exercise required to get and stay healthy might surprise you.

According to Ayurveda, which is the longest-running health system of the world, most people should not even do prolonged strenuous exercise. Half the battle of losing weight is taken care of by eating the right foods.

This is why in holistic health, it is so important to eat right as well as move your body, so the two can work together. As a result, you won't find yourself struggling. All you really need are these three forms of activity;

- Movement
- Aerobic Exercise
- Strength Training

First, let's cover daily movement. Sitting is one of the worst things you can do. If you are standing or moving around regularly, you are off to a good start!

If you sit at a desk for your job all day long, see if you can get one of those adjustable desks to set your computer on. Or at the very least, stand up and stretch every half hour, or even better, go for a short walk.

Being moderately active for most of your day is easy to do if you aren't a couch potato. But if watching TV is your weakness, consider doing your workout while watching TV. Or have your shows on while you are cooking or doing the dishes.

I make it a point not to sit on my couch until my day is winding down. I even work on my computer standing up. Try to aim for no more than 2 hours a day in a sitting position if you can help it.

Swimming and bicycling are a few of the more fun exercises that are good for your muscles and your heart. Exercising outdoors or in water have multiple benefits.

One thing I do, which helps keep me moving on a regular basis, is jumping on a mini-trampoline, otherwise known as a rebounder. You don't even have to jump; you just have to bounce, not even lifting your feet off. What this does is activates every cell in your body. This is the best way to move your stagnant lymph and help your body detox. The lymph system has no pump, so it relies on us to get it moving. Only a few minutes a day can do the job, but I find this so fun I do it for a few hours every day sometimes.

Try to avoid having an erratic workout schedule. Commitment is necessary if you want to get real results from your workout. Setting a specific time for exercise is the best approach for it to be effective. Try to set a schedule you can stick to. If you commit to three evenings per week, make it happen.

Another tip is to vary your exercises and workouts. Choose activities you enjoy so you can look forward to having a more active lifestyle rather than just dreading workouts. Listen to music or podcasts, so you don't feel like you're only exercising. Getting the mind engaged in something can act as a distraction from the effort your body is going through. This is something I do, and it really helps me work out longer when I lose myself in what I'm listening to.

Aerobic exercise is anything that gets you breathing and gets your heart rate up. Many activities count as aerobic exercise, and some of them are fun! Take your pick!

- Walking
- Running
- Cycling
- Swimming
- Jumping Rope
- Cardio Machines
- Hiking
- Dancing
- Cross Country Skiing
- rebounder/trampoline

This is just a short list to give you some ideas. It's a good idea to do at least 30 minutes a day of aerobic exercise on most days of the week. Walking is also easy to fit into your day since you can do it almost anywhere, almost anytime, even in short bursts.

Even if you aren't training to be a bodybuilder, it is still essential to keep your muscles toned. Muscles also burn more calories than fat. You lose what you don't use, so only 30 minutes 2-3 times a week is all you need. If you do strength training every day, be sure to work different muscle groups, so everything gets a day to rest. To make things simpler on yourself, do strength training every other day, alternating with aerobic.

You don't have to lift boring weights if you don't want to! Here are a few examples of ways to work your muscles;

- lifting weights (had to include it!)
- resistance bands
- stairclimbing
- cycling
- dancing
- push-ups and sit-ups
- yoga
- rebounder/trampoline

Since spirituality is a huge aspect of holistic health, I can't leave out the category of spiritual workouts. Think of them as exercises for your soul that use your body as the middleman.

You might be aware that yoga has spiritual benefits as well as physical. Qigong is another activity that falls into this category. Qigong (and its relative Tai Chi) are movement exercises that stimulate the flow of energy in and around your body.

Qigong, Tai Chi, and yoga combine deep, slow breathing with body awareness, leading to spiritual benefits, similar to meditation. These have multiple health benefits;

- Lowers blood pressure
- Improves balance
- Reduces stress
- Improves your immune system
- Reduces chronic pain

CHAPTER 7

Why Connecting to Nature is Crucial

You may not realize why connecting to nature is so important; after all, it could be days or weeks or even months before you step foot outside, and you don't notice anything wrong. You aren't sick, so why worry, right?

The effects of nature deprivation aren't immediately noticeable, and they affect the body, mind, and spirit. They slowly creep up on you in the background while you go through the day to day grind of your life.

Your life demands all your attention, so it slips the minds of most people to put nature on their priority list and set aside time for it every day. The spiritual aspect of your health can especially go unattended if you are busy trying to improve your physical, mental, or emotional health.

Humans are just like trees and plants; we need to be connected to the ground, we need the sun and water to grow, and the air to breathe. Unfortunately, spending the majority of our time indoors doesn't allow us to get sunlight, the grounding effects of the earth, or fresh air. And without those things on a regular basis, our soul also suffers.

Humans are made of nature, namely the five elements; water, air, earth, fire, and space. Sometimes it is shown as metal, instead of space. The metal version refers to the Earth's elements where space is more of a spiritual aspect of it.

Water. Everyone knows we need water to drink, and that our bodies are made mostly of water. It carries nutrients to our cells, helps eliminate waste, and regulate our body temperatures.

Air. Without the ability to breathe clean, fresh air, we die. Not only does air provide oxygen for our cells, it also plays a huge part in our weather systems. Nature depends on air, and all living things in nature depend on air.

Earth. The Earth provides us with nourishment and medicine. The earth also has an energy of her own, and we can tap into it if we touch the earth with our bare skin. The earth's energy is grounding to us, binding us with nature.

Fire. On a physical level, fire is a chemical reaction. It is symbolized in the human body by creativity and passion. We also cannot live without the sun's warmth and light.

Space. This is what holds it all together, as well as being pure potentiality. **Metal** is the hard substances that are formed from the Earth in the form of minerals.

The simplest method of connecting to nature is to **go for a walk**! Easy, free, and it works every time! If you live in a cold climate and bundling up doesn't sound appealing to you, I understand. I live in Minnesota, where 1/4 of the year, it is almost dangerous to be outside. In the winter, we have to get creative.

Meditation in nature can be even better than indoors if you aren't around other people, barking dogs, traffic, and power lines. The more natural, the better!

Camping is one of the best ways to connect to nature since it forces you to get up with the sun and learn to cook things by the campfire.

Hiking is another excellent choice, as it incorporates exercise and a connection to nature.

Gardening is probably the most rewarding method of connecting to nature. Having your hands in the dirt, sitting on the ground, and eating the fruits of your labor is probably the best way to achieve a connection with nature. And you get the added bonus of your food being more nutritious.

If you're not afraid of thunderstorms, **walking in the rain** or standing under a roof outside during a storm is probably my favorite way to connect to nature. You are literally inside all the energy nature is releasing. It is such a powerful experience! Of course, be safe about it and don't stand under a tree or carry anything metal on you, if there is lightning.

Swimming in a lake is an excellent way to connect to nature, especially if the lake is somewhat clear and not polluted. There is something special about immersing yourself in water outside.

Walking along the sandy beach is one of the best ways to ground yourself since there is so much water mixed in with the sand, which helps your body absorb the Earth's electrons. Grounding is so good for us; it is recommended that we do it every day if the weather allows. It has a massive amount of health benefits, including helping you sleep better, reducing inflammation in the body, and reducing pain. By walking barefoot on the Earth, we are forming a connection to nature that is not only literal but crucial for our health!

One hobby that definitely helped me with connecting to nature was **nature photography**. Photographing nature brings you deeper into it. Rather than just passing through, you are creating art out of a moment in time. It's amazing the mindset you can adapt when heading outside with a camera. Even mundane corners of your neighborhood can hold lots of gems if you just keep a mindful eye.

Let's face it, 90% of the time you're outside, are you really peering up the trunk of a tall tree? Do you ever stop to marvel at the layers of color and depth that cover almost every square foot of outdoor space?

It sounds cliché, but you develop more of an appreciation for nature when you are forced to find beauty in it. I hope I can inspire you to venture out with a camera, and just try to keep up with the photo opportunities that seem to come out of the woodwork when you immerse yourself deep enough.

You don't have to be a pro with a fancy camera. Some of my pictures were taken with $30 gift cameras I got for Christmas and birthdays. Some were taken with a pretty top of the line Nikon but honestly, what matters is your creativity and your eye. A camera can't take a picture that your eyes fail to see first.

If you ever have a few hours to kill, daytime or nighttime, there are endless works of art to find and capture…get out there, and you will feel so connected to nature when you are done, you'll have a huge smile on your face, you'll feel energized, and you won't be able to wait to discover more places!

Connecting to nature can be a struggle if you live in a cold climate or are house-bound for any reason. Here are a few ways you can bring nature indoors.

Keep plants and flowers indoors! Not only are they good for the air in your home, but they help you feel connected to nature. If you don't get enough sun where you are, the pothos plant is really good at thriving even without constant attention and sunlight.

Watching nature documentaries is always a joy, or just having a calming nature video playing while you meditate or relax.

Use a Himalayan salt lamp. These lamps are made from actual salt blocks taken from 5000 feet down into the salt caves; they are hundreds of millions of years old! It's really cool knowing something that ancient is in my house. What these do is ionize the air, which helps you breathe easier as well as gives you a calm feeling. You know how awesome it feels outside after a thunderstorm? Everything is crisp and clean and refreshing, well, there's a reason for that.

Before a thunderstorm, the air is filled with positive ions. After the storm passes, the air is filled with negative ions. It sounds backward, but negative ions are a good thing! A Himalayan salt lamp does this exact same thing indoors.

Another cool thing about these is that they incorporate ALL four elements! Earth is the wood base, Air is what it purifies, Water (in tiny amounts) attracts to it when it is turned on, and Fire is from the heat from the light inside.

CHAPTER 8

How Your Environment Affects Your Health

Toxicity of our environment is one of the ways that our cells malfunction and make way for disease and illness.

The bad news is our water, air, food, and hygiene products are all being tainted with toxins. The good news is our bodies, if healthy enough, can fight against them.

The even better news is that there are a wide variety of ways you can avoid these toxins, and a wide range of products you can use that are not toxic. If you educate yourself, you stand a pretty good chance of winning your body's war against toxins.

Your environment affects your health in a myriad of ways. It's no secret that our carbon dioxide levels have risen due to the modern world we live in. Pollution and electric power lines are a double whammy.

It's also no secret that our water supply is no longer safe to drink out of the tap. Also no secret is the fact that our food is being grown using pesticides, insecticides, not to mention the lack of nutrients in the soil due to failure to rotate crops properly.

And lastly, most of the mainstream products out there that we put on our bodies every day are made with so many chemicals, plastics, and toxins that it would make your head spin.

We simply cannot achieve optimum health by breathing polluted air, drinking tainted water, eating poisoned food, and slathering chemical-laden products on our bodies. It's no wonder our poor immune systems are failing; they cannot keep up with the onslaught of toxins. They never get a break!

We aren't even safe inside our homes, with off-gassing of paints and furniture, EMF's from our wi-fi, mold growing in our walls, the list goes on. What can we do?

Let's just be clear about one thing right now. You cannot eliminate toxins completely from your environment. It's a shame, but our world is too far gone, and at this point, all we can do is try to minimize the damage.

Let's start with the air. While there is nothing the average person can do about the overall quality of the outside air, there are some things we can do about our indoor air.

Air purifiers are practically necessary these days. You can buy one to fit any budget, but the most expensive ones will obviously do a better job, removing pet allergens, toxins, and odors. You want to find one that has a HEPA filter, which stands for high-efficiency particle air. Also, make sure you buy one best suited for the room size.

Another solution to indoor air pollutants is to have an indoor plant. There are a few kinds of plants that are especially good at sucking the bad stuff right out of the air. These include;

- garden mum
- pothos
- spider plant
- ficus
- peace lily

- Boston fern
- snake plant
- aloe vera
- bamboo palm

Using beeswax or soybean candles instead of paraffin candles is better for the environment. Paraffin candles release toxins when burned where the other two kinds do not.

Essential oils are good to use in a diffuser to purify the air. Look for these scents which work the best at getting rid of toxins in the air;

- Lemon
- Cinnamon
- Eucalyptus
- Tea Tree
- Rosemary
- Wild Orange
- Lavender
- Pine

Opening your windows regularly is also essential. If you live where it gets cold in the winter, try to air out your home as close to winter as possible and as early as possible in the spring. As bad as the environment as a whole is, getting fresh air from outside to come into your home is still the best option.

Using the right cleaning products goes a long way towards not adding additional toxins to your indoor air. To many people's surprise, air fresheners are actually harmful to you! Many of the chemicals in those spray fresheners are hazardous, so don't even use them at all. Essential oils add a lovely scent to your home while also detoxifying the air.

There are some environment-friendly cleaners out there; you just have to find them in places like health food stores. If you really want to go the natural route, you can make your own cleaners with ingredients you probably have around the house.

Here's a basic recipe for an excellent all-purpose cleaner;

ALL-NATURAL ALL-PURPOSE CLEANSER
1/2 cup white vinegar
2 TBS baking soda

10 drops of lemon or tea tree essential oil

Mix the vinegar and essential oil in a spray bottle, then add the baking soda and mix well. Then add some water to fill the bottle to the top.

You can also use liquid Castille soap (Dr. Bronners is a pretty popular natural soap) mixed with baking soda along with your choice of essential oil.

If you require a more powerful cleaning action, you can add Borax to your baking soda/vinegar/oil mixture.

Just like the foods we eat, the cleansers we use work best when they are kept simple and natural! Why use nasty chemicals when we don't have to?

Another thing we have to worry about in our environment is EMF's. Electromagnetic Field Radiation is a pretty scary thing, yet nobody really takes them seriously. This is perhaps the most dangerous aspect of our indoor environment. Some people are more sensitive to this than others.

Everyone knows that cellphones emit EMF's, and we can't really stop using them in this day and age, so what can we do?

Some options are to put your phone on airplane mode when you are not using it. If you don't want to miss calls, you can just set it away from your body as much as possible.

Avoid talking on the phone, since holding it up to your head for long periods does the most damage. So text instead of talk, if you can.

And above all else, avoid sleeping with your phone. The further your phone is away from you when you sleep, the better. In fact, this rule goes for all electronics. Sleep is when your body is healing and rejuvenating, so it is very detrimental to your health to be surrounded by electronics as you sleep. Even having your phone on the other side of your bedroom is good enough.

Try not to stand near appliances when they are operating, such as the dishwasher and microwave. Even your computer puts off EMF's. I have mentioned grounding/Earthing, and one benefit of grounding is the drastically reduced amount of EMF's in the area that is grounded.

They make grounding pads for you to use indoors that will give the same effect as grounding outside. The object is to have your bare skin touching the mat while you are using your computer, and it will protect you from the EMFs coming from your computer.

Another trick is instead of having a wi-fi router, use an ethernet cord for your computer. This seems like a hassle having a long cable going across your living room or kitchen, but if you can eliminate as much wi-fi in the air as possible, you'll be better off.

Off-gassing is another hazard in our air. You may not have heard of off-gassing, but it is a very real and scary thing. Anytime you buy new carpet, furniture, or paint that is not natural, off-gassing occurs for a while. All these things are made with chemicals, and the fumes escape into the air for a few weeks or months in some cases.

There was the case of a young child who became seriously ill when her parents had all new furniture in her bedroom, along with fresh paint on the walls and fresh carpet. The off-gassing made her sick, and she did not get better until they had her sleep somewhere else.

Not everyone is this sensitive, but children and the elderly are especially susceptible. It is a good idea only to buy one new piece of furniture at a time, and if you can, make sure the air movement in the room is adequate and that you spend as little time in there as possible while it is off-gassing. A general rule of thumb is to give it about a month before it is considered safe.

New cars are notorious for this (and we all love that new car smell, don't we?), so it is best to drive with the windows down as much as possible when your car is new.

Natural hygiene products are important in fighting toxins in our environment. Your skin, your largest organ, is very absorbent. Whatever you put on it will get inside. You may wonder how you didn't get sick from all the unnatural junk you have been putting on your body your whole life. Well, in small amounts, the body can generally do a good job of getting those toxins out. But it is hard on your body. Give your body a break by using all-natural hygiene products.

There is a natural version of everything, so there is no excuse to poison your body anymore. And remember, just like with our food and cleaning products, anything you put on your body is best when it is simple. Natural and simple go hand in hand.

Many foods are even good for the skin, including lemon juice, raw egg whites and yolks, yogurt, mashed up cherries, oatmeal, honey, apple cider vinegar, and many more. Castille soap is good for cleansing the face, and you can add natural oils such as Vitamin E or almond oil (both great for skin). Bentonite clay is good to use as a mask to draw out dirt and impurities and detoxify the skin.

There are thousands of all-natural recipes that are just a google search away, but I want to give you a few to start with that are basic and simple to make.

ALL-NATURAL SHAMPOO
1 TBS of baking soda
1 Cup Water

RINSE
1 TBS apple cider vinegar
1 Cup Water

It will not lather up, but the chemicals that cause the lather you don't want on your head anyway. Getting used to no lather is hard, but just think of all the toxins your body won't have to deal with anymore! The vinegar smell is nothing to worry about it; it doesn't linger after you are done. But if you like, you can use a few drops of essential oil to give it a scent.

ALL-NATURAL DEODORANT
3/4 cup arrowroot powder
1/4 cup baking soda
4-6 TBS melted coconut oil

Mix baking soda and arrowroot powder.
Add 4 tablespoons melted coconut oil and mix. Add more coconut oil until you like the consistency.

ALL-NATURAL TOOTHPASTE
4 TBS Coconut Oil
4 TBS Bentonite Clay
2–3 TBS water
1/2 tsp sea salt
10–15 drops peppermint essential oil

Mix coconut oil, clay, and salt in a bowl. Begin with one tablespoon of water. Mash the ingredients together and add more water until you get the consistency you want. Add in the peppermint oil and then mix well.

CHAPTER 9

Natural Healing Modalities

There are many natural healing modalities for those who want to utilize them. Conventional medicine is necessary for a few things, like emergencies and serious medical conditions. But when it comes to preventing chronic diseases and acute illnesses, going the natural route is better for your health overall.

Alternative medicine shouldn't even be called alternative since it was the original! All the ancient cultures used natural healing modalities, and the fact that we are the most unhealthy humans that have ever existed is proof that we need to go back to nature.

Natural healing does just that, it heals. Pharmaceutical drugs never cure you. They even make you more sick with all the side effects. They are not natural, so the body cannot heal on its own like it was designed to do.

The body needs the right nutrients, and it needs to be as free of toxins as possible. Then it can heal. It is your job to make sure the body can heal itself, not make its job harder by giving it a constant stream of poisons. By viewing drugs as a last resort, you may be able to cut down on the pills you take. That can save you money and reduce the risk of side effects.

Naturopathy is a broad term for the study of healing that focuses on nature. It includes a long list of specific healing modalities. I will give a basic rundown of each of the main ones here.

Ayurveda means "science of life," and it has been used in India for a few thousand years. It is the only complete health system that is based on the body, mind, and spirit. It is truly the best option for a holistic-minded person.

Ayurveda incorporates many things to promote balance for holistic health. Here is a list of just a few habits and routines used in Ayurveda;

- oil massage
- enemas
- nasal rinsing
- tongue scraping
- dry brushing
- yoga
- herbs and foods right for your body/mind type
- living in rhythm with the sun
- oil pulling
- meditation
- chewing thoroughly
- drinking warm or room temperature water before meals
- sitting while eating and being mindful while you eat
- walking daily, especially after eating
- eating only what is in season
- correct food combining

Reiki is an energy-based healing modality in which the practitioner directs energy through the recipient's body.

Reiki has its roots in India. Dr. Mikao Usui, a Japanese doctor on a quest for spiritual healing, came upon a 1,000-year-old Buddhist manuscript detailing many healing methods. The word "Reiki" means Universal Life Force Energy.

On the emotional level, Reiki heals by dissolving the blocks we create through our negative judgments and thoughts. This "stuck" energy frequently appears as illness in the body.

Reiki is very effective for emotional and mental balance. Regular treatments will ensure that you don't easily get stressed out. With mental balance comes better memory and clarity.

Acupuncture is a Chinese therapy that uses very fine needles focuses on stimulating specific healing points along the energy meridians of the body. Acupressure is the same thing only using your fingers to apply pressure on these points.

Iridology is the study of the iris. Once you learn what to look for, you can look up close at the iris and tell what state of health certain parts of your body are in.

Hypnotherapy, using hypnotism for healing, is done mostly for mental and emotional issues, such as quitting smoking or losing weight. You can also perform hypnotherapy on yourself; this is called auto-suggestion.

Reflexology involves applying pressure to certain areas of the hands and feet. Certain areas of the hands and feet are directly connected by nerves to organs, and by applying pressure to these areas, healing can take place.

A common way of utilizing natural healing is for colds and the flu. When you have a cold or flu, your body is going through a natural reaction to a virus. These reactions need to run their course; this is why it is not suggested to suppress your symptoms with cold and flu medications. Natural healing is so important when you have a cold or the flu.

At the first sign of a cold, start doing these things, and in most cases, this will shorten the length of your cold or flu, and lessen the severity as well;

1. Rest. When you have a cold or flu, be sure to get more sleep than usual. Take naps, sleep longer when you go to bed, and in between, don't do anything strenuous. In fact, just getting up and walking around can drain you if your cold is bad enough. Our bodies communicate with us by giving us a feeling, and we need to honor that feeling. If you feel exhausted, your body needs rest, plain and simple! In fact, lack of proper rest is a huge contributor to colds and flu. The immune system works best while you are sleeping.

2. Get plenty of fluids, namely water and tea. Soda, energy drinks, or coffee are not proper fluids when you are sick. Also, make sure the fluids are warm or hot. Drinking bone broth or chicken broth is also an excellent way to help your body heal itself.

You can also drink apple cider vinegar, the taste is harsh, but you can mellow it out if you dilute it with water and/or add honey or lemon. Taking this in a small shot glass is the perfect size, and you can do this a few times a day.

3. Oil of Oregano is an excellent antimicrobial and antiviral treatment, so it is good to take when you are sick. Take 1-2 drops a day and make sure it is medical/food grade.

4. Zinc fights colds and flu; you can take this in liquid form mixed with water or in lozenges.

5. Eat good. If you have a cold, eat things like chicken soup, fresh fruit, and vegetables. This is not the time to be eating pizza, burgers, and doughnuts.

If you have the flu and are vomiting, only drink broths, tea, and water. Once you feel you can handle solid food again, start with something like oatmeal or fresh fruit.

6. Garlic is good for the immune system, and if you aren't cooking anything, you can still get some garlic by chewing on a small piece (harsh, but some people swear by it!) or chopping it up and putting it into your tea. You can also grind it up fine and spread on bread.

7. Honey is full of antioxidants and also has antiviral and antibacterial properties. Therefore, it is invaluable to your immune system. Take by the spoonful a few times a day.

8. Eucalyptus oil. If your sinuses are clogged, Eucalyptus oil works wonders! Put a few drops of the oil in a diffuser or even a bowl of steamy water and breathe in the steam. A neti pot also works great for the sinuses.

9. Ginger is one of the best spices when you are sick. Using freshly grated ginger in tea is best. Ginger is especially useful for nausea, so it is a perfect tea to drink when you have the flu.

10. Vitamin C, of course! Last but certainly not least, up your intake of Vitamin C in the form of fruit, if possible, or supplements if you don't have fruit handy.

CHAPTER 10

Our Five Daily Needs

No matter what your lifestyle goals are, if you are a human, your basic daily needs are ideally these five things;

- Sleep
- Water
- Nourishment
- Exercise/Movement
- Sunlight/Fresh Air

I know many people live without these things occasionally, so this doesn't mean you will die if you don't do all five of these things every day. But to live a healthy, happy life, every day should include these things.

Our daily need for adequate sleep is crucial. If you are one of those people who say, "I'll sleep when I'm dead.", you will sooner rather than later learn this lesson the hard way.

After 24 hours of sleep deprivation, you have the cognitive impairment of someone with a blood alcohol content of 0.10 percent, according to a study published in the International Journal of Occupational Medicine and Environmental Health.

Your memory and judgment also begin to suffer. After two days of not sleeping, the body will start to force you to sleep, and you will start to blackout and be disoriented.

After a few days of no sleep, hallucinations will occur. Clearly, sleep is one of the daily needs humans have that we should never mess around with.

Sleep is vital to your health and happiness. Generally, the younger you are, the more sleep you need. Babies sleep most of the time because their bodies are still building, and sleep is when most of our healing, rejuvenation, and mental processing takes place.

Adults need between 7-9 hours a night, on average. Everybody is different, of course. If you have set work hours and kids to raise, it is not likely that you will be able to adjust your sleep schedule. But you can take steps to increase your chances of getting quality sleep.

1. **Make your bedroom your sanctuary**. Declutter your bedroom, so you feel calm upon entering. Set up a small area to write in your journal, meditate, and any other relaxing activity. I have a few Himalayan salt lamps in my bedroom, and a tapestry of a forest scene to gaze at while I meditate.

2. **Keep your room dark**. Your body is designed to sleep when it's dark. Use room darkening shades if you have to. Be aware that any light you can see is registering into your mind. Light from outside such a street light should be blocked out. Remove as much artificial light from your sleeping environment as possible. Paint your walls a darker color, I have done this in all the bedrooms I have had except for one and that one is where I got the worst sleep.

3. **Exercise during the day**. Most forms of exercise will pep you up and give you more energy immediately afterward, so make sure you exercise well ahead of bedtime. Plan your exercise routine either in the morning or afternoon or at the very least, 3 hours before bedtime.

4. **Make yourself a bedtime routine**. Allow your body and your mind time to unwind. If you're super busy, you'll probably be rushing around until you finally collapse on the bed in hopes of getting a few hours at least. Instead, give yourself at least an hour to shift gears and relax before bed. Create a bedtime routine that involves things that make you tired, such as soft music, a warm bath, light reading material, meditation, or journaling. Many people take showers before bed, but showers are more stimulating than baths. Sitting for a few minutes in warm water can help your muscles relax and prepare for sleep.

5. **Turn off electronics at least one hour before bed**. The light emanating from backlit screens like cell phones can trick your body into thinking it's daytime. It's best to rest your eyes from bright screens before trying to sleep. Don't watch TV for the last hour or two before bed. Television stimulates the mind too much, which can cause difficulty sleeping. It is good advice to keep the TV out of your bedroom. Using a cellphone in bed is also a big no-no, especially if you don't have a blue light blocking app on your phone.

6. **Leave daytime stress outside your bedroom**. In order to rest, you'll want to put aside things that keep your mind whirling. Write down your to-do list for tomorrow before you start winding down for bed. That way, you know you have gotten them out of your head, so you don't need to even think about tomorrow. Make sure you've dealt with all the questions that keep you awake, like what bills need to be paid, what time the doctor appointment is, etc. This frees you up for sleep.

7. **Try to go to bed at the same time every night** and get up at the same time every day. If you get in the habit of going to bed at a particular time, your body will expect to be sleeping. Your body is much more efficient at sleeping and preparing for sleep if you can maintain a schedule. Rarely is it possible to be perfect at this, but a half an hour in either direction won't matter too much.

8. **Keep your bedroom cool**. Sleep quality is improved in a cool sleeping environment. Your body temperature drops around bedtime and is at its lowest during sleep. If the room is too warm, your body won't be able to cool down. Just think of how hard it is to sleep on a hot, humid summer night when just touching your sheets is almost unbearable. And then think of how comfortable it sounds to sleep wrapped in thick fluffy blankets from head to toe like a cocoon! It is much easier to sleep when you can curl up surrounded by blankets! Go cool enough to be comfortable but not so cool that your nose is cold to the couch. I have found that between 60 and 65 degrees works best.

9. **Avoid alcohol**. Alcohol can help you fall asleep, but sleep quality is significantly compromised.

10. **Take magnesium**. Magnesium works on the nervous system and helps you reach a state of calm.

11. **Don't eat right before bed**. Your body takes hours to digest food, and this takes energy. If your body is digesting food while you are sleeping, it will have less energy to put you into the restorative mode. However, some foods are more difficult to digest than others. Stick to simple dinners and eat them as early as possible. Avoid heavy meats and creamy foods. If you find your stomach growling right before bed, have some raw almonds, popcorn, or something light. This isn't the time for a heaping scoop of ice cream or fruit that has natural sugar in it.

12. **Get a white noise machine** or use a fan. The sound of white noise is amazing at blocking out intrusive sounds and putting yourself into a trance-like state.

13. **Drink a hot beverage before bed**. Warm milk or decaffeinated tea like chamomile will work great! Just don't have too much, or you will be waking up in a few hours to use the bathroom.

14. **Lavender essential oil** is really good for relaxing before bed.

15. **No electronics**. Rid your bedroom of as many electrical items as possible or switch them off. It is especially important not to have your cellphone charging near your bed. I turn mine off at night while it is charging on the other side of the room.

16. **Do some light yoga before bed.** There are many gentle yoga styles that focus on light stretching and breathing techniques. These only take 10-15 minutes and can be done just before bed.

17. **Listen to relaxation CD's.** These range from soothing music tracks to the sounds of ocean waves. These sounds have a particularly relaxing effect and will also help you sleep more soundly.

Another thing that is equally as important as sleep is water. We are made of mostly water, so it makes sense that one of our most important daily needs is to drink a lot of water, especially if we live in a hot climate and/or exercise a lot every day. Many people think that a few sips here and there is good enough, and I hate to be the bearer of bad news, but it is not good enough. Most people are dehydrated, often not even realizing it. The sensation of thirst means you are already dehydrated. Not getting enough water can cause headaches, muscle cramps, and constipation. Aim for 6-8 glasses a day, possibly more if you live in a hot climate or exercise frequently.

The quality of water you drink matters too. Tap water has been shown to have a spectrum of toxins in it, including birth control pills, arsenic, and radioactive contaminants. No matter what side of the fluoride controversy you are on, the previous three I mentioned should scare the crap out of you.

Buying a cheap filter in your local store is not good enough. These don't remove enough of the bad guys. It might sound impossible for you to afford a decent water filtration system, but when it comes to the most important thing you are putting into your body every day, what it comes down to is how much your health is worth to you.

Reverse Osmosis systems do a pretty good job, although the downside is this process removes everything, including the good guys, minerals. Calcium and magnesium are among the minerals that your body needs every day. If you drink reverse osmosis water, you can buy trace mineral drops and add a few drops to each glass. You can also sprinkle some Himalayan salt in your water.

Spring water is really the best water you can get. You can buy it or find a spring and collect it yourself.

Water that is stored in plastic should be kept in a cool dark place. Light and heat are not good when it comes to plastic bottles; anything stored in them will get traces of chemicals from the plastic leeched into it.

So ideally, your best bet for getting safe water is spring water stored in glass jugs and bottles.

Another crucial daily need is sunlight. It is necessary for Vitamin D. Our bodies can assimilate it much easier in the form of the sun than from food or supplements. It's unfortunate, but you can't even get the amount you need in a day just from food alone. And supplements out there are pretty iffy, many of them not even being the right form of Vitamin D. What we need is D3, not D2. And contrary to what people believe, you cannot get Vitamin D from sitting indoors in sunlight, because glass blocks the UVB rays.

We can get enough Vitamin D each day if we go outside in the sun for a short time. You can get more Vitamin D if more of your skin is exposed. Also, you can get more Vitamin D if you get sunlight in the middle of the day; however, this is when it's easiest to burn. So be careful not to be in the sun for the entire duration of mid-day (10 am to 2 pm).

Where you live also makes a difference. Naturally, people nearest to the equator can make more Vitamin D from the sun. People living in cold, cloudy climates will definitely need to take supplements.

And lastly, the color of your skin also matters. The paler you are, the quicker your body will produce Vitamin D.

As a general rule, try to expose as much of your body to direct sunlight as possible for short periods. Work your way up to longer periods, if you are pale or already not tan. Don't let yourself burn.

There is a sweet spot where you get enough Vitamin D and do not burn. This sweet spot is different for everyone, so start slow and find out where your sweet spot is.

Some studies show that sunscreen protects against skin cancer, but other studies have shown it does not, and some even say it causes cancer with all the chemicals in it. Personally, I would rather cover my skin than put anything with chemicals on it. You can also rub coconut oil on your skin, this does a good job of protecting from burns, and it's natural! You can also use Red Raspberry Seed Oil, Shea butter, or Carrot Seed Oil.

In addition to the daily needs I have discussed in this chapter, exercise and proper nourishment from food are also included in this list, which are covered in detail in other chapters.

While we're on the topic of daily needs, I have a question for you to answer to yourself. Do you enjoy routines? Even the word "routine" sounds negative, but not in this case! These routines are grounding, healthy, and fun! Why is a daily routine important? We are what we repeatedly do. Just as one piece of chocolate cake isn't going to add pounds, and neither will eating kale once take the pounds off.

Building a lifestyle routine is a commitment from you to your body, mind, and soul. If you want changes to happen, regularity is vital. The trick is to find actions that are enjoyable to you, or at least that you are willing to work through to get your desired result.

I will now lay out some daily routine options for you. You can pick and choose any that you want to implement into your lifestyle; you don't have to do all of them. But the more you do, the more you will be living in harmony with nature and will have more optimal health.

Building a lifestyle routine is fun, so don't feel overwhelmed by this list! Not everything will be a good fit for you; however, you should at least try each thing a few times to see if it is something you think you could do regularly.

1. **Wake up as early as you can**, ideally in time to watch the sunrise. We are creatures of nature, and nature revolves around the rhythm of the sun and moon. Many people work nighttime hours or have sleep disorders that prevent them from rising with the sun, so I understand this one might not be possible for you.

2. **Scrape your tongue** first thing when you get up. Have you ever really looked at your tongue? Chances are, you have a coating on it. This coating varies in color depending on your constitution and the level of toxicity in your body. What this coating is made of is a toxic substance that the body creates due to unhealthy food choices. It is a thick, sticky, smelly substance that you do not want in your body. If you have a very thick green, yellow, or brown coating, that means you have a high level of toxins in your body. The tongue scrapers that work best for this are made of copper or stainless steel. Also, by scraping your tongue, you will taste your food better. Taste is more than just for our enjoyment; taste is part of the digestive process. When the tongue recognizes different tastes (bitter, sweet, salty, pungent, sour, and astringent), it produces certain enzymes to digest them.

3. Brush your teeth and then do a practice called **oil pulling**. This is swishing around in your mouth, either sesame oil, coconut oil, or a mix of the two. What this does is pulls impurities out of the mouth naturally and gets rid of harmful bacteria. Oil pulling has been a practice in the Ayurvedic tradition for thousands of years. Fifteen minutes is ideal, but anything is better than nothing. Important; do not swallow the oil when you are done. It is full of bad stuff; you don't want that in your stomach. Also, it is advised not to spit it in the sink because it can clog it. The garbage can is ideal.

4. **Drink a hot liquid,** either tea or lemon water. This gets the digestive system ready and stimulates the bowels. It is best to have a bowel movement in the morning before eating breakfast.

5. **Meditate, do yoga, or both.** I like to do these at night, but it is often advised to do them in the morning if you have time.

6. **Dry brushing.** Our lymph system has no pump, so the only way our lymph (which carries toxins out) can get moving is if we exercise or do something called dry brushing. You may have heard of this, but for those who haven't, it's basically brushing your dry skin with a special brush that you can find in the health section of most stores. This stimulates the lymph system as well as removes dead skin cells. Do this before showering. In a few weeks, you will be amazed at how soft your skin feels!

7. **Eat mindfully.** When eating breakfast (or any meal, really), be sure you are sitting down. Chew thoroughly, the whole purpose of saliva is to break down your food to prepare it for the stomach. If you don't chew good enough, your stomach has to work harder to break down your food, and this can result in some of your food not getting fully digested. This leads to gas and constipation. Also, when you are eating, you shouldn't be doing anything else, so this might be a tough one to get used to. It is best to gaze off into the distance (outside, ideally), and take your time, really paying attention to how the food tastes and feels in your mouth. Mindful eating tells the body you are calm, and this helps the body digest much easier.

8. **Take a 10-15 minute walk after eating,** if you can. This stimulates digestion and gets things moving. But don't do any strenuous exercise.

9. **Lunch should be your biggest meal of the day.** When the sun is at its highest, this is when our bodies naturally have the most digestive power. If you are going to eat meat, do it at lunch when the body has ample time afterward to digest it. Undigested meat is one of the worst things to have sitting in your intestines.

10. If you can, **get your exercise in between 10 am and dinnertime.** The middle part of the day is when our bodies are burning the most calories. You could even exercise before 10 am if you have the time and motivation. I like to start my day off slowly and not do anything too strenuous until the middle of the day. But some people have more energy in the morning.

11. **Eat a light dinner 3 hours before bedtime.** Dinner should be lighter than lunch, and no closer to bedtime than about 3 hours. I think 2 hours is ok if you have a quick digestion and metabolism. But if you are trying to lose weight, you don't want to eat within 3 hours of bedtime at all, especially if your dinner was on the heavier side.

12. **Watch the sunset,** if possible. Actually seeing the sun go down is the best way to prepare your body for a good night's sleep.

13. After dark, **start cutting back on blue light**, from cell phones, computers, and the TV. If you must use these things, you can get blue light blocking apps. I use this on my laptop; it is an app called Flux. You can personalize it to start blocking more blue light, depending on when your bedtime is. I also have amber light bulbs in my home, which give off a more calming, pleasant light, which is similar to candlelight. This signals to the body that bedtime is nearing. Lighting candles or even having a campfire in your backyard is also good to do in the evening after dinner.

14. **Get your thoughts out.** Write down your to-do list for tomorrow. Write in your journal everything that is on your mind to get it onto the paper and out of your head so you can wind down for the night. Winding down for sleep happens much easier without the mental clutter.

15. After clearing your mind, do any of the routine nighttime items, which include a warm bath, meditation, light yoga, reading, etc.

CHAPTER 11

How Mental and Emotional Health Affect the Body

The body-mind connection is real. When one is down, the other is likely to follow. Most people are aware of the mind-body connection and how important it is to be mentally and emotionally healthy. But there is so much more to having a healthy mind that most people either don't know about or they pass it off as unimportant or irrelevant to their health. Many aspects of the mind play a crucial role in holistic health.

I like to think of the mind as having three branches;

- Mental & Emotional Health
- Consciousness
- Mind Expansion

Of course, mental and emotional health are the most influencing aspects of your mind. Stress affects us mentally and emotionally and, eventually, physically. And since most people have stress in their lives, this is an epidemic that needs attention.

Stress is the reason behind most doctor visits and is partially to blame for the six leading causes of death. Let that sink in.

Therefore, taking control of your mind and emotions is crucial. It sounds easier said than done, but once you learn the ways you can improve this aspect of your life, you will become motivated to make it happen.

The mind is the part of us that connects our body to our soul. You can think of it as a middleman. This is why expanding our mind and consciousness are necessary for true holistic health.

Consciousness is pure awareness, which makes us become more mindful. To be "awake" is to be aware of yourself, to be mindful of your behaviors, your thought patterns, your choices in life that shape who you are and how your life unfolds.

Diving into the subconscious mind can also be very powerful, therapeutic, and life-changing. Putting yourself into altered states gives us a respite from the outer world and can get us in touch with our true selves.

This is why having a healthy mind is so crucial for us to reach optimum holistic health so that we can develop our soul, our spirit. Most people never reach this level of consciousness.

If you remember the diagram of Maslow's Hierarchy of Needs that I shared in Chapter 2 about physical health, you will now see why taking care of the body and mind comes before taking care of your soul. Getting in touch with your soul is the ultimate destination of personal development and self-actualization.

Expanding your mind is like stepping out of your comfort zone in a sense. It is about admitting you don't know everything and finding the motivation to learn. Growth of the mind is the only way we can become well rounded. We should never stop learning and growing and evolving. Thinking outside the box is necessary. Creativity, growth, and wisdom are the result of an expanded mind.

Just the fact that you are here reading this book is a sign that you have an open mind, which is a good prerequisite to living a holistic lifestyle.

The subject of consciousness is so fascinating to learn about, and if you don't know much about it, you are in for a treat! If you've seen the movie Inception, you can recall how they experienced a dream within a dream. Consciousness is like the same thing; only it happens while you're awake, so it is being aware that you are aware.

If you remember Maslow's hierarchy of needs regarding the lower end of the pyramid, there isn't a whole lot of consciousness happening at the bottom. Most animals and other life forms are on this level. Most wildlife forms aren't conscious of most of the things humans are conscious of. To be aware that we are aware is truly the pinnacle of human evolvement and something we should all strive for.

You might hear of people describing themselves or others as being "woke," and a lot of people have negative connotations with this term, which I believe is just due to their ego feeling the need to judge something they don't fully understand.

Here's another fascinating thing about consciousness; imagine you're driving down the road and suddenly realize you don't remember the last 10 miles. You were so lost in your thoughts that you were not mindful of what was happening.

Being mindful is a type of meditation, to put 100% of your attention on a single task. This is the opposite of multi-tasking, which is not very practical in this modern world we live in today.

However, the mind gets stressed easily when it is overloaded with information. This is why we feel a sense of calm and inner peace when we go out in nature and just sit. There is nothing to do except be. The mind loves this. This is the first step to higher consciousness, to clear the mind.

Altered states of consciousness are another aspect of the mind that is fascinating. They say people who are depressed are living in the past, and people who are anxious are living in the future. So, what does that make people who live in the present? They just are. In the present moment, everything just is, with no worries, no regrets, only pure being. This is why altered states are so enjoyable. Once you take away thoughts, you're left with an empty space of awareness.

Getting into an altered state is easier than you might think. Of course, one often-used method is to use drugs to reach that point faster and effortlessly, but we want the natural approach.

There are a few that I find always work. The sound of **steady drumming** is one of the best ways. You can get yourself a drum and do it yourself, but I suggest finding videos on YouTube. This way, your hands are free, and you can meditate while doing this, or dance, however, your body wants to express itself. During this trance state, the brain goes into alpha mode. This is an excellent time to either give yourself affirmations or to focus your intention on something you want to manifest.

Slow, rhythmic breathing is another way to enter into an altered state. This is why this is so important to do when you are meditating.

Dancing is probably the most fun way to achieve an altered state. This works best if the music holds a steady rhythm. Doing this in a place where you can close your eyes is even better. Music is one of the best focusing activities for the mind.

Getting into an altered state is the key to reaching your subconscious mind. Hypnotism is often ridiculed, but people aren't usually aware that most of us get hypnotized every day without realizing it! You can get hypnotized by the highway as you're driving, by the tv as you're staring at it barely blinking, by music that is repetitive and goes on long enough to pull you into a trance.

When we are in this state, the subconscious mind is accessible. You can take charge and reprogram your habitual thoughts, any trauma you have had in your life, and direct your mind to manifest your dreams.

Another method of reaching your subconscious mind is to **lucid dream.** This is a hard skill to learn, but if you can master it, it will be a massive benefit to your life.

Studies have shown that things like learning and therapy can take place in this state. You are essentially able to do anything you want, so there is no fear. And since you are aware of it, it is pretty much like a real experience, which becomes a real memory once you wake up, as long as you can remember your lucid dreams!

I can't talk about the mind without bringing up meditation. Meditation is scientifically proven to reduce anxiety, depression, stress, insomnia, pain, and the list goes on. The list of benefits is immense, and no doubt you are aware of this.

So, how can you meditate? What if you hate sitting still for long periods? What if you are too busy? What if you have tried it and it is boring to you, so you gave up? There are solutions to all these problems.

Putting yourself into an altered state is a great way to get your foot in the door of meditation. Once you have calmed your mind easily, you have done all the hard work.

I have tried the traditional way of meditating, sitting in the lotus position, eyes shut, fingers touching, in silence, trying to stop my thoughts. This may work for some people, but not all. If meditating this way has never worked for you, read on!

Meditation through music is probably my favorite way to meditate, because music is one of my biggest passions but also because you can't help but get transported to another realm. But there is a trick here. Most people listen to music in the background while they're doing other things, or they listen to music for entertainment. The type of music that works for meditation is not the same stuff you hear on top 40 radio stations.

The three elements of music are rhythm, harmony, and melody. What is essential for meditative music is only rhythm and harmony: the beat, and the main body of sound. Melody usually refers to the vocals or a single instrument that stands out above the rest.

What we are looking for here is something rhythmic and calming; ambient music, Shamanic drumming, etc. But you can also use different genres, such as rock, if the particular song has the right elements.

I avoid songs with lyrics as this distracts you from the movement of the song. You want to focus on the beat and the overall flow of the instruments. Classical works for some people, but for me, it tends to be too erratic. I find songs work best if they flow; if they have a steady rhythm.

A good test is if you can sway back and forth to it. Become one with it, and don't be doing anything else. It doesn't even have to be upbeat music; you can "dance" to slow music too, even music without a beat. Sway your arms as if you were directing the flow of air. Imagine the energy around you and imagine yourself interacting with it.

Another great way to meditate is by using your senses. This was a powerful technique that I learned from a book I read years ago; I believe it was a book on lucid dreaming. In lucid dreaming, you are aware within your dream; you know you are dreaming. Becoming aware is a crucial skill to have in lucid dreaming as well as waking life.

To do this, you can be anywhere doing anything; it doesn't matter. You go through each sense and focus only on it. For example, what do you see around you? Find something in your field of vision of every color and focus on everything you see that is that color. Focus on each texture you see.

Then move on to hearing and become aware of every sound you hear. You will be surprised at how many there are.

Then move on to what you can taste, if you are eating. Same with smells, usually nothing will be too apparent unless you are cooking or near a bonfire, candles, etc.

Then focus on what you feel, how your clothes feel, how the air feels on your skin, etc. Really soak in everything you can sense through all your senses.

This exercise imprints this moment into your memory very strongly. The first time I did it was years ago, and I still remember every detail. Being aware of everything your senses are picking up is a great way to feel connected to nature, or wherever you are, and will also distract your mind from your worries and leave you very calm. From this point, you can easily enter into meditation, or just use this itself as the meditation.

Driving is very meditative, with or without music playing. Everyone feels better when they go for a drive and crank the music. But sometimes it's very calming to turn off the music and just focus on the road and the hum of the car. It's also particularly meditative when there is light rain.

One time I drove with the radio off for about 2 hours when it was lightly raining, it was very calming and peaceful. Just a safety reminder; make sure you are using this as more of a mindful meditation as opposed to a trance-inducing one.

This next method of meditation kind of goes along with music, but it's separate because it isn't music. It is called brainwave entrainment. You must listen with headphones. You can buy cd's or mp3's or entire programs based on this technology. YouTube is filled with them. Search for "binaural beats."

The basic concept of these programs is to put your mind into different states. Mostly alpha or delta, which are the states where your brain is in a state of relaxation. A popular company that does this is called Hemi-Sync.

The first time I ever listened to one of their cd's, my awareness was lifted out of my body. Not like an astral projection exactly, I couldn't go anywhere or see anything in another room, I just had a powerful sense that I was bigger than my body. I just felt huge; I felt like the whole universe in my mind. But the minute I moved a body part, the feeling went away. So, it is very important to be as still as possible while listening to these audios.

Using imagery is a technique that works quite well for mediation. When my mind is racing too much and I need to fall asleep or calm down, I will imagine I am a giant mountain in the middle of the open sky, nothing but me and the clouds. I imagine myself so tall that clouds are floating by my head. Then I insert my thoughts into each cloud as it passes, and that's all the time I am allowed to think each thought. Then I imagine a gap in the clouds where I can regain myself and think no thoughts for a few seconds.

As this state never lasts long anyway, I give myself permission to think a new thought as long as I pause in between and wait for each cloud to pass.

This method also teaches you to let things go. I am a fan of Buddhism, and letting things go is a very Buddhist thing to do, and very good for your mind!

Guided meditations are another method, and this is pretty self-explanatory, but in case there are any real beginners here, I'll explain. This is where you listen to audio that guides you through every step, including telling you what to visualize. These are excellent for anyone who can't stand not having something to focus on and listen to. You can find thousands of these on YouTube for free.

Mindfulness meditation is another method, and this is similar to the senses one I mentioned, except instead of expanding your awareness to everything you can sense, you simply concentrate your awareness on one single thing. It could be a thing you are doing, such as doing the dishes. It could be a thing you can look at, such as a candle. Candles are perfect for this and probably why they are used so often in churches, rituals, and spells. Humans are drawn to fire, and whether it's a small flame or a roaring bonfire, the mind will start to calm when you look at it.

One of my favorite meditation methods involves nature. Nature is conducive to meditation because all the things that cause stress are because of our modern life, work, home life, technology, etc. Once we remove ourselves from our man-made world, our minds can finally stretch its legs and relax! It is much easier to do the traditional sitting meditation if you are outside in a calm environment. Just stay away from factories, traffic, barking dogs, power lines, and anything else disruptive.

Meditation and stress reduction go hand in hand, so it's worth mentioning this here. Since stress is responsible for most illnesses, doctor visits, and (some claim) causes of death, stress reduction is crucial! Everyone has too much stress in their life unless you are a Buddhist monk, which is highly unlikely.

Getting regular massages is a great way to reduce stress. Most places give you a discount if you go more regularly. If you have a partner, take turns giving each other back rubs or even full-body massages.

Soaking in a bubble bath is also up there on the list. Of course, many people are too busy with kids, their job, cleaning the house, making dinner, etc. but even once a week is better than never. Give your bath time some oomph by adding Epsom salts, which are detoxifying, or lavender essential oil, which is relaxing. Listen to calming music or a guided meditation.

Laughter is an overlooked medicine, and it's totally free. Watching a funny movie can bring almost anyone out of a stress-induced funk.

Aromatherapy can be used while doing any of these suggestions. Getting an essential oil diffuser is like bringing the spa experience right into your home. There are hundreds of scents to choose from, depending on your mood and specific issue you are dealing with that day.

This next suggestion may not be possible for everyone, but I have found that the best stress beater is silence. If you live alone, this is easy, peasy. It is incredibly calming to just be in silence.

This doesn't have to be a meditation; you can just sit in a comfortable spot, in silence, looking out the window. This can work outside if you live in a rural area where you can't hear traffic and have few or no neighbors.

Watching less TV, or the news specifically, works wonders for stress. The news is mostly bad anyway, and who needs that kind of negativity in their life? Surely not someone who is trying to live a holistic lifestyle!

Don't worry; you will still know what's going on in the world (if you have Facebook, there is no escaping that!), friends and family will talk about things, so you have nothing to lose by turning off the TV except your stress. This can also go for TV shows, not that anything is wrong with having your weekly shows to keep up with but try to keep those activities to a minimum.

If you are an introvert, you can get stressed out a lot easier than extroverts. Be sure to give yourself enough alone time each day (or most days of the week, if need be).

Another crucial step in reducing stress in your life is eliminating toxic relationships. Relationships, unfortunately, are a significant cause of stress in our lives. Many people settle in relationships that are not good for them or don't know how to deal with toxic people in their lives.

We must learn personal boundaries, and to put our well-being first. It is not selfish to take care of your mental and emotional health; it is not selfish to reduce stressful relationships in any way that you need to. As they say, you can't pour from an empty cup. You can't give with no one giving to you in return.

If someone is causing you more pain than pleasure, more sadness than happiness, more anger than joy, re-evaluate this relationship. You can cut back on time you spend with toxic people without cutting them out of your life.

Reducing work-related stress is a biggie. Finding a job that you enjoy is probably one of the most significant components of mental health. Besides sleep, you spend more time working than you do on any other single activity. Many people even spend more time at their job than they do sleeping!

If your job makes you miserable, your mental and emotional health is sure to suffer. If you are just in a job for the money, just imagine how it would feel to have a job that you are excited to go to every day!

Most people never think twice about this. They get a job out of necessity. Imagine having a job that you choose, or better yet, create!

If the problem is a co-worker, see if you can move to another department or office away from that person. If you can, use some calming essential oils while you are working.

Stress reduction is possible at work, but in the end, you have to decide if the job is worth it. I have had some pretty stressful jobs and left every single one of them. I know not everyone can do this, but life is short, and you have to ask yourself if you have looked hard enough for a job that is right for you.

Starting your own business is always an option, even if you don't think you have what it takes. There are lots of ways to earn money online so you can work from home. Spend a week or two researching all the possibilities and let yourself dream!

Or maybe your current job will let you work from home a few days a week, or every day. This is a more common occurrence these days due to much of our work needing to be done on a computer.

Think outside the box. Create your dream career yourself if you have to! Start a side job in an area you are passionate about. Take a life purpose course if you don't know what your passion is, and find a job in that field, or create it!

Finding balance is essential when it comes to stress reduction. We have to find a balance of work and play. The more play, the better! Don't feel guilty for playing.

Find the time to nurture relationships, nourish your body, sleep, travel, and enjoy your hobbies. If any one thing begins to take over your life, bring it back into balance. Set up a daily routine, so you make sure you get enough sleep, mealtime, family time, self-care time, and time for your hobbies.

The reason why people feel burnt out is because something is getting out of hand, most likely the demands of your job or the time you are required to spend there. Don't let any one aspect of your life go out of balance, or you will feel uneasy, stressed out, and it will affect your life before you are aware of it.

You are probably familiar with the yin yang symbol. In Chinese philosophy, this is a symbol of complementary opposites. These opposites also have a small aspect of the other within it. If the balance gets tipped, dis-ease will result. Nature is always in balance, and we must strive to achieve harmony and balance in all aspects of our lives to prevent stress and illness.

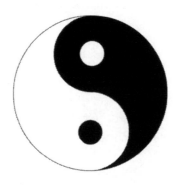

CHAPTER 12

Why is Personal Development Important?

The term personal development can mean anything that helps you grow and evolve. It requires expanding your mind and shifting out of your comfort zone.

This requires effort, which is hard for a lot of people. It is easy to be overcome by outside thoughts and not think for ourselves. It is too easy to be programmed by the words of society and not hear the words coming from our mind. It is easy to remain in one place for too long and not see a need for change.

To have an open, expanded mind is essential for the overall health of your mind and the soul. It helps you recognize new possibilities and opportunities. It helps you achieve success and a higher purpose. Thinking outside the box brings many rewards.

It also propels our society forward, which cannot happen without people who dare to be different. Your comfort zone may be safe, but it is not conducive to growth and evolution.

It is a healthy mindset to know that there are always things to learn. Constantly seeking knowledge is not only smart but also keeps you humble. A lot of people may be turned off by the thought of learning as an adult. "Didn't we already graduate high school?", you may ask. This is not memorizing dates, names, and places. This is an extension of soaking up information like a child does. We should never lose that child-like curiosity about the world.

The world is far vaster than most of us could ever experience in our lifetime. The way I see it, if we cannot experience it firsthand, we should at least strive to learn about it in other ways. Every day we should have an open and curious mind to soak in anything new we discover. Being well-rounded helps us be the best version of ourselves that we can be. This is why personal development is so important.

Some people go back to college as an adult. If this is not possible, the next best thing is to take online courses, which comes in many forms. There are lots of online course platforms such as Udemy, where you can learn almost any subject you can think of for a relatively low price.

You can also take classes at local community colleges. Many of the courses and classes found online and in community colleges will give you a certificate, diploma, or degree. But it is not necessary to earn those if you want to gain knowledge for personal development.

Books are another great way to learn. You can buy old textbooks if you want comprehensive information organized all in one place. Or you can just read various non-fiction books about the subjects of your choice.

Audiobooks are even better; you can learn while you're driving to work, or doing housework, or in the shower. Most of the time, I have something playing, if I am doing a task where my mind can focus on what I am listening to.

YouTube is even a wonderful place to find things to learn. It isn't all about entertainment. There are also colleges that post their lectures online for free.

Documentaries are one of my favorite ways to learn and expand my mind. Movies are generally known for their entertainment factor, but since I have gotten more into documentaries, that is what I prefer to watch now. Why just be entertained (which is kind of a loss of your time if you think about it), when you can learn at the same time?

Seminars, lectures, conferences, and workshops are more immersive ways to expand your mind and learn new things. Some of these aren't cheap, but many of them end up on YouTube or through the website of whoever put it on.

The importance of creativity and expression should not be underestimated. Doing anything creative is a great way to step into personal development. When you are in the act of creation, you are in a receptive state of mind to whatever ideas flow to you. Expressing ourselves is good for the soul and your health.

There are many means to do this, through visual arts, through writing or playing music, through poetry, through invention, through building things, through creating new recipes, the list could go on forever.

Many people think they are not creative, but I believe this is only because they haven't done the right kind of self-analysis. A lot of "non-creative" people focus on others' ideas rather than diving deep into their minds to discover their own. When one is fully relaxed and receptive, creativity is natural and effortless.

Sit down with a pen and paper or paint and canvas. Buy a musical instrument you've always wanted to learn. Take art classes.

Spend more time doing things you love to do. It's so simple, yet so many people don't do it. What makes you happy? Spend more time doing it.

As people grow older, it seems they naturally gravitate towards the couch and away from their hobbies. Another benefit of being holistically healthy is that people naturally find themselves doing more things they enjoy rather than ingrained unhealthy habits.

If your growth is important to you (as it should be), travel can accelerate your personal development. Travelling gives you a complete picture of the world, so people who travel a lot are very well rounded. They have seen different cultures, different lands, and had many experiences that cannot be had otherwise.

When you travel, especially to other countries, you find that materialism is overrated. When you travel abroad, it's not easy to bring your book collection, big screen TV, and fine silverware with you. You quickly realize that you can do just fine without all of the items you seem to love so much back home.

You also see other people living perfectly happy lives with very little in the way of possessions. Different cultures have different priorities. While our society values fame, fortune, possessions, and other forms of material success, many other societies have little concern for that sort of thing.

There are a lot of people in the world that don't have the basics. We take many things for granted. There are people that walk 20-plus miles each day just for water. You can see people living with dirt floors or playing soccer with a ball made of empty water bottles. It's easy to forget how the rest of the world lives.

Making new friends in other parts of the country or world is one of the best ways to broaden your perspective. You don't have to limit your friends to those people you see at work. It's possible to create and maintain friendships across the globe. It's easy to stay in touch these days with all the technology available.

When you travel, you learn to be flexible. Many things are less reliable than in the western world. From bus schedules to electricity, it's not uncommon to have your plans disrupted on a daily basis. You will learn to be more flexible and creative. You can even bring that new skill home with you.

While you are traveling, you realize that you waste a lot of time when you're at home. While you're traveling, you won't want to spend your time staring at your smartphone or watching TV. You'll want to be out living and experiencing the local scene. You'll realize how much time you waste back home doing things that provide little value to you.

Speaking of other countries with few possessions, this brings up the subject of minimalism. This is actually a trendy subject in developed countries now, and for good reason. While minimalism isn't one of the main aspects of holistic health, the mental benefits cannot be denied.

Why is minimalism so good for mental health? Think of meditation. When you are meditating, you are either trying to empty your mind or focus your mind on one thought at a time. This is what leads to a relaxed state, lowered blood pressure, and other health benefits.

So wouldn't you want your physical world to be relaxing like your mental world when you are meditating?

Most people can agree that multitasking can be stressful. Balancing two or more activities at the same time can be draining. The mind can only handle so much stimulation. When the mind is overstimulated, it can shut down. So naturally, you can see where this would have the same effect on the body. Your body and your senses can only handle so much at once.

It is physically impossible to listen to two things at the same time, you can hear both things, but to mentally focus on two things at once cannot be done. Just try to watch a TV show while someone is talking to you, you have to choose which one to focus on at a time.

Likewise, your eyes can see peripherally many things, but it cannot focus on more than one object at a time.

Clutter is toxic to the eyes in a mental way. Would you rather walk into a storage room with all your junk shoved into every crevice with barely a path to walk around? Or would you rather walk into a room with one small chair and one small table with one candle on it with one book sitting on the table? The mind is drawn to simplicity and order and is repelled by clutter and chaos.

Most definitions of the word "minimalism" use the word "simplicity." That is really the essence of it. Why would you want life to be anything other than simple?

Minimalism does not require you to live out of a backpack, nor does it require you to throw out your book collection or all your fancy kitchen gadgets.

Go back to the essence, simplicity. Give your mind less to focus on. Give your body more space to move around in. Give your eyes less clutter to sort through. Give your life a spring cleaning!

I'm going to give you a simple 3-step plan on how to become a minimalist.

1. **Assess your life and narrow it down to what really matters.** Sit down with each collection you own and ask yourself if you get real value out of owning it. Ask yourself if you would rather have the extra space and money you would get for selling it. Imagine your life without this stuff and try to feel if you would miss it.

Try to narrow down your collections to just a few. You don't want to be one of those people who collect things just because you want to be able to say you own every single related item that has ever been made. Don't let your belongings own you! Keep the ones that embody your essence.

If you are a photographer, by all means, keep every lens you have ever bought! If you are a chef, don't feel guilty keeping all your kitchen toys! If a collection of items is actually useful, this counts as adding value to your life.

2. **Start with a small space and work your way up.** It's a huge motivation booster to see what one small area can do! Start with one corner of a room and slowly work your way to the whole room.

3. **Organize what you have decided to keep.** An organized area is much more pleasing to the eye than having things scattered around willy-nilly. If you have to, buy or build shelving, or a closet.

Once you minimize your belongings, you might want to keep going! Here are some general suggestions for other ways to minimize your entire life.

When going through your clothing, it is more efficient to have fewer items of clothing but to have items that you can mix and match with each other. This is called a capsule wardrobe.

For example, have one or two of each item (such as a skirt, jacket, long sleeve button-down, etc.) and having them color coordinated so they can go with anything. That way, you can build many variations of outfits with less actual items.

Many people tend to have double of things, especially when it comes to kitchen items. You really only need one of anything. Choose whichever one is more versatile, or whichever one is more regularly used. You certainly don't need five frying pans of the same size or three different sets of measuring cups. Aim for quality here, and you won't need the quantity.

When it comes to the items in your bathroom, it becomes easier to clear more space if you start making your own beauty and hygiene products. You can get by with just 5-10 items rather than 30. With just some Dr. Bronner's soap, baking soda, and a few different oils, you can make almost everything you need.

Consider digitizing your music, movie, and book collections. This one is a bit hard for a lot of people because it is nice to have a physical book in your hands, or to sit back and visually see all your CD's or DVD's organized alphabetically. But if your extra space is important enough to you, and you don't mind switching to a Kindle, mp3 player, or streaming device, it will feel like a weight lifted off your shoulders.

Look more into reusing, recycling, and re-purposing. It's better for the environment and gives you a sense of being resourceful. There's already enough garbage and junk in the world; let's make it a better place by reducing our need for new things.

Of course, things like your vehicle and major appliances shouldn't be from the 1980's, but don't go overboard and feel like you must have the newest biggest size refrigerator that makes it's own ice cubes.

Tiny houses are a big hit with the minimalists. You can also live in an RV if traveling is your thing. With either of these options, you can still store some of your belongings at a relatives' house or in a storage facility.

These options are growing in popularity and not just with retirees! With more and more virtual jobs, increasing numbers of younger people are opting to live simply in a tiny home or RV so they can move wherever they want.

With lower living costs, this appeals to many minimalists, who can then focus more on the things they enjoy. Why pay for a huge house if you don't need all the space? Why spend all that extra time cleaning when you could spend it relaxing?

Living in a smaller space is an excellent way to consume less. If you don't have the room for a bunch of crap you don't need, you aren't contributing to consumerism. Is your life really better after you buy your 13th lamp? Wouldn't you rather take a vacation instead of having a room full of gym equipment that you only use sporadically?

And you can't take it with you when you die, so why leave a load of junk for your children who don't have room for it either? When you have fewer things, you can have more experiences; less stuff=more life.

Minimalism is one of the best things for the environment because are you contributing less to the landfill and garbage problems in the world.

Living sustainably is one of the end goals of many minimalists. It is also the lifestyle of many people who are into holistic health and environmentalism. Being completely sustainable is quite the process, though, so if you aren't able to live off the grid right now, there are many other things you can do in the meantime.

Building a homestead might not be an option for everyone. But it's worth looking into if your goal is to own a house.

Living off your land not only gives you control and freedom over your life, but it also puts you in the best position in the event of power outages on the main grid, or if the economy collapses and the world descends into chaos.

You can use solar panels, wind turbines, or generators to provide your house with power. These are costly to set up, but are cheaper in the long run, not to mention you won't have to worry about major grid shutdowns that will affect everyone except for you. And doesn't it sound great to imagine being immune to food shortages? You can just step outside and pick your dinner from the garden.

Alternative transportation is another excellent way to help the environment and live minimally. You could get rid of your vehicle altogether, if you can use public transportation, or walk or ride a bike regularly. Carpooling, whenever possible, is another option. If you must have a vehicle, you can trade down to something more fuel-efficient. Smaller vehicles use less gas and are also quieter.

If you have less stuff, you are probably using less electricity. Gadgets and appliances are an energy suck, so the less you have of them, the better. Or at the very least, don't have them all running at the same time.

This is another pleasant side effect of living in rhythm with the sun when you are awake for more of the daytime; you won't need to use your lights as much.

CHAPTER 13

Spiritual Health; Evolution of Your Soul

You might already have a sense of spirituality in your life, or you might need some guidance regarding spirituality. Many people fall into this last category, and if that's where you are, you're not alone.

The hectic demands of modern life have made many people feel disconnected. Achieving a spiritual connection will bring about a sense of balance and peace in your life.

Many people confuse spirituality with religion and believe that spiritual health can only come from religious beliefs. However, spiritual balance comes from more than subscribing to a religion. Some people do seek religion for their spirituality, but spirituality can also be achieved without belonging to a specific religion.

Essentially, developing spiritual wellness means working toward identifying what you believe in and how well those beliefs can give you inner strength and peace.

When you've developed spiritual health, you can understand the meaning of life and become in tune with the purpose of your existence. And as a result, you can lead a more fulfilling life.

Many people don't even think about life purpose, let alone know what it is. They follow all of society's unwritten rules, in the order everyone else does them, and absorb thoughts and ideas that are not their own in the form of entertainment, "education," advertisements, and others' opinions.

Achieving spiritual health is not easy these days. But it is necessary if you want to live a truly holistic lifestyle.

People who have connected with their soul are infectious to be around. They say you are the average of the five people you spend the most time with. If you want to evolve spiritually, you must look around you and be careful who you are surrounded by.

How many people do you know take classes for the sole purpose of learning something they are interested in, not because it is required for a degree they need to get a certain job that society tells us is respectable?

How many people do you know who ooze their spiritual truth at all times, not merely attend Sunday church because they were raised that way, regardless of how they treat people any other day of the week?

How many people do you know build a lifestyle around their life purpose and their passion(s), not just claiming any random job or life path is what they were meant to do?

It is highly unlikely that you know many people who fit those criteria. Don't get me wrong; I am not saying those are bad things; they are just further down the pyramid of human consciousness and actualization. Everyone has room for improvement.

So, how do we achieve spiritual health? Each of us is responsible for developing our spirituality in our own way. Your chosen path may take you on a different journey than another's.

To begin your journey toward spiritual health, question the purpose of your existence. Ask yourself a few key questions as you go on a quest to achieve balance through spiritual health.
Self-exploration is the key to developing your spiritual balance. Ask yourself what the purpose of your existence is on the planet. What things, people, and ideologies do you feel drawn to?

Becoming spiritually healthy involves believing in something. It consists of identifying your purpose and working towards achieving that purpose. Most importantly, it involves becoming truly happy with your life. Ultimately, the balance you seek will come when you satisfy your spiritual needs.

Achieving spiritual health isn't an overnight process. With persistence and dedication, you'll find yourself connecting with another aspect of your existence that you never realized. More and more things will become clearer to you, and you'll start to experience true inner peace, no matter what challenges you're faced with.

Holistic health has a lofty end goal; to become the best version of yourself you can possibly be, physically, emotionally, mentally, and spiritually. You are reading this because you have that spark in you that a lot of other people don't have, or at least don't have the motivation to improve. You could say your higher self leads you here. Don't let him or her down!

So, what exactly does the word "spirituality" mean? Those that claim to be "spiritual but not religious" account for over 20% of the population in the United States. But what does that even mean?

The word spiritual is used to describe that which relates to the human spirit. It goes beyond the material. It is your connection to the divine, source energy, God, a higher power. No matter what name you give it, it feels the same.

It can come from a religion, from nature, or something else entirely. But everyone needs something to believe in, to connect to. Spirituality should be a personal thing for each individual. You might even change your beliefs a few times in your life, which is great! I believe people should question things and expand their minds to allow for other viewpoints.

I was raised Catholic, but it never sat well with me, and in my 30's, I discovered Wicca and really resonated with that for many years. Now I have expanded and refined my beliefs to be centered around nature, energy, and vibration.

I realize some people out there may disagree with my definition of Wicca, but that's the beauty of it. One of its branches is called eclectic, which means the practitioner considers themselves solitary and follows whatever resonates with them. It's generally considered the "religion" of nature.

I, among others, don't consider Wicca an actual religion. It is not about worshiping a being who created you; it's about respecting and honoring the nature you were created with. It's about honoring the God and the Goddess, the male and female energy of the Universe. It's not about evil spells and sacrificing animals, it's about positive intentions and respecting all living things, most of all the Earth itself.

The five elements that make up the points in the pentagram are Earth, Water, Air, Fire, and Spirit. You might remember how Earth, Water, Air, and Fire are the four elements of the physical universe. So, it's clear to see how Wicca is a natural practice, not man-made or dogmatic.

Wiccans celebrate the equinoxes and the solstices; they celebrate the moon, the powerful energy of thunderstorms, and all other things about nature.

The negative stereotype against Wiccans is very unfortunate because we all honor nature to some degree. It might be more subconscious in others, but I believe every human has at least once been in awe at nature and felt truly one with it.

This generally happens as a child then gradually fades as we age, only coming to a peak again as we are closer to death. This only shows even more how we intuitively know we are a part of nature, we came through it and will return through it time and time again.

Paganism is a broad umbrella term that is used to describe Earth-centered religions. There is another "religion" based on nature, and that is Pantheism. The name itself means that everything is God, meaning the whole Universe. Pantheists are nature worshippers. Unlike Wicca, they don't believe in many gods, nor do they perform rituals (although some probably do). Pantheism is mostly defined as simply reverence for the Earth and nature. The Native American tradition is also very nature-based.

Everything in nature is energy-based. We know through quantum physics that what we perceive as matter is just energy vibrating at a lower level. Everything is energy; everything is vibrating on a cellular level.

This may be blowing your mind right now if you don't study this field, but it is a foundational aspect of holistic health, so it is crucial to understand. Your spirituality might even come from science, and that is ok too!

The body is the temporary physical manifestation of energy, the mind is what shapes us by directing our energy and attention on growth and change, and the soul or spirit is the life force, the highest vibrational aspect of us that never dies. Energy cannot be destroyed; it can only change form.

Taking all this into account with everything I have learned, it makes the most sense to me to believe that we are energy beings incarnate on Earth in a body that we must take care of. Since the body is made of elements just like everything else in nature, it only makes sense that we align ourselves with nature as much as possible to stay healthy.

Living a lifestyle in tune with nature is something so essential to spirituality. Everyone feels it the minute they step into a forest or near water. There is a thing called forest bathing where just being in a forest for a certain amount of time brings you back to a state of balance, peace, and harmony. Nature heals us.

We have no idea how far gone we as a society have come regarding nature. We have no grounding connection anymore, most of us don't see the sunrise or the sunset (and some see neither!). We don't eat foods in season, which affects our health.

Entire books have been written about this subject. It is massively underestimated how vital nature is to us. We ARE nature. To separate ourselves from it is such a travesty, yet we continue to do it.

A huge sign that humans have lost their way with nature and spirituality is the fact that ancient civilizations used to build temples that worked in harmony with the sun (Stonehenge, for one). Now humans barely even know what these sacred sites were used for! We need to get back in touch with the stars, with the sun, with our Earth!

Here are some easy ways to put a little nature back into your life;

- Alter your schedule around so you can watch the sunrise and the sunset
- Walk barefoot on the Earth for a minimum of half an hour a day (called Earthing, or Grounding)
- Eat foods only in season
- Sleep outside
- Cook outside
- Bring plants inside
- Plant a garden
- Take daily walks around your neighborhood, preferably near water or lots of trees
- Go swimming in a lake instead of a pool (chlorine, yuck!)
- Gaze at the moon and the stars every night (if it isn't cloudy!)

After integrating nature into your life more, you will start to feel something. Life seems to have more meaning when we expose ourselves to nature on a regular basis. No wonder our ancient ancestors were so spiritual; they were always outside!

You may have purchased this book because you were only interested in the health aspect, and don't feel like you have a spiritual bone in your body. That is ok! Or you may just have not developed it yet even though it is lurking under the surface.

For many years I focused on partying and going to movies, not giving much thought to any of this. But I always had an affinity for spiritual things without being full-blown spiritual. I collected a lot of angel statues, tarot card decks, candles, etc. Those things are fine but are really just tools, and anything can be used as a tool.

What really counts is that you feel a connection to whatever you feel is the higher power of creation. What counts is that you love and respect all living things with a sense that we are all one.

Here are a few of the things you can incorporate into your life to develop your spirituality;

- prayer
- meditation
- journaling
- going on a spiritual retreat
- fasting
- volunteering
- creative activities
- yoga

Awakening, or enlightenment, is the slow process of evolving spiritually. It has many definitions and traits and can vary from person to person. But everyone has the potential for full enlightenment, so there is no judgment on anyone who hasn't started the awakening journey yet.

It sometimes starts with a significant life event, usually a bad one. Some people have near-death experiences or lose everything they own or suffer extreme emotional loss. These things can change a person's life and perspective almost immediately.

For others, it can simply be a slow casual process, such as a natural inclination towards researching the truth about reality. The right book can be a gateway for someone.

Meditation and yoga can be good starting points. There are also many spiritual retreats around the world if you are looking for a deeper immersion, which would most likely give you better results.

It is fairly common for people to feel isolated when they are going through an awakening process. They are outgrowing their old life to the point that they no longer feel satisfied with certain parts of it. They may want to spend less time with the same people, doing the same things, and going to the same places.

It is also hard to find others to talk to about your newfound beliefs, experiences, and perspectives. Most people want you to stay you, and if you change so much that you aren't the same person anymore, this will no doubt cause problems with the people in your life who you have known for a long time.

However bad as this sounds, this is a good thing. This is a sign that you are evolving. Humans were not meant to be stagnant. If you aren't growing, you're dying. Energy must keep moving for us to stay healthy. We should always go with the flow and not fight what feels natural.

This is where trusting your intuition comes in handy. You should always go with your gut. Pretty obvious, I know, but most people seem to go along with what everyone else is doing, think what everyone is thinking, buy what everyone else is buying, etc.

Enlightenment requires a good dose of self-love, so you can think for yourself and have the courage to evolve in the way that feels right to you.

Once someone is comfortable with their spirituality, their enlightenment, or whatever awakening they have gone through, the right people will find you.

This is what "your vibe attracts your tribe" means.

We are the average of the five people we spend the most time with. If you feel yourself not vibing with your usual scene, it means you are on your way up to a new one. Don't fight it. We can't evolve and change without some awkward growth spurts!

Have you ever become addicted or obsessed with discovering new spiritual teachers? You'll get into one, and they lead you to another, and before you know it, you feel overwhelmed with all the information.

Some of it even contradicts each other, and you wonder which one is right. You want to believe all of them, but they don't all agree, so you can't. Well, honestly, that's ok.

I believe that the purpose of spiritual teachers is only to broaden your mind and spark thoughts inside of you. I don't even believe 100% of what all of them say; I just go with what resonates with me at the time.

Maybe you don't agree with much of what one guru says, but there is a particular message that really means a lot to you at a particular time, then accept that. You can take bits and pieces of different messages from different gurus and compile your own personal belief system.

I believe there is only one basic necessity when learning new teachings. I keep an open mind and consider the possibility that something is true, and then kind of forget about it while taking the parts that I know I believe and live by those.

Then, maybe someday down the line, I will hear that message again, and perhaps that second time will do the trick. Or it might take three or four times from different teachers before I add it to my belief system. Or I might never subscribe to it, and that's ok.

A huge part of spirituality is being your own guru. I think it says a lot about a person when they form their own beliefs rather than blindly accepting everything they hear. I believe spirituality is a personal "religion." It's a personal belief system made up of the parts that make sense to you.

All that being said, I still believe it's a good thing to explore different teachers and take as much from them as you can.

CHAPTER 14

Why a Life Purpose is Necessary

If you've ever been dissatisfied with your life and thought, "There must be something more," you're absolutely right. There's a whole lot more.

Learning about yourself and your place in the world might even be the true meaning of life. But that's for you to decide and discover.

Your soul is crying out for you to discover why you were put on this Earth. It wasn't just to work a job you hate, pay bills, and die. Most people have the desire to find their life's purpose at some point, but in most cases, it is suppressed by society.

Why are YOU here? If you haven't found your life purpose yet, have no fear. Most people haven't.

Most people let this simmer in their unconscious mind, choosing to push it aside, ignore it completely, or they feel like they just weren't born with a purpose. Living a life in that mindset is not holistically healthy. We want you to be different!

You were created with a set of passions and talents that make you unique when combined with your personality traits. Discovering your purpose in life lets you use your unique personality, skills, abilities, and interests to bring you greater self-fulfillment. When you're doing what you feel like you must have been born to do, you can live a life you created, not just a life you feel was handed to you.

Sometimes the thing that holds you back from self-discovery is a fear of change. There's comfort and safety in not taking risks, but you also may never discover your life's true purpose.

It can take a lot of work to find it. Nobody can find your life purpose for you. It requires self-awareness and self-analyzing.

You may be one of the lucky few who knew what their life purpose is at an early age and are also lucky if that doesn't change over time. Those people generally don't have to struggle so hard.
But for most of us, we either have too many obstacles or too many ideas of what our life purpose could be.

There are many books and programs out there to help you find your life purpose. But if you can't afford it or don't have the time, here are a few ideas which are also quite fun!

Try **volunteering** if you have the time. Find an organization in your community that interests you. Doing something worthwhile can be a good way to discover your purpose. This is also a good way to get your feet wet in a career without having to spend money on schooling or waste time working at a job that you decide isn't for you.

Ask yourself some important questions; When anything is possible, what would you do? What would you do if you didn't have to worry about money? What do you love to do so much that time seems not to exist when you are doing it?

What change are you passionate about seeing in the world? What unique skills and personality traits do you want to incorporate into your life's purpose? What would you do with unlimited amounts of money once your survival needs have been met?

Explore a new hobby or an old one that you pushed aside. We all have at least one activity we've been putting off until a more convenient time. Doing something new and different exposes you to new ideas and thoughts.

Some people have too many hobbies and interests and can't decide which one to pursue. In this case, you can take into account other factors such as which ones fit in with your education, skills, and talents. Or which one fits best with the lifestyle you want to live, what your ideal day and lifestyle would be like.

Start a vision board and display it where you will see it every day. Vision boards are something you can attach pictures, quotes, words, or anything else that you want your ideal life to include. Just be sure also to spend time taking action and being on the lookout for opportunities in the form of baby steps to your goal. A fulfilling life of purpose doesn't usually happen overnight.

Get a journal. Write in it either first thing in the morning or last thing before bed, when your mind is calm and stress-free. Write down what your ideal day would be like. Project yourself into the future and imagine that your life is virtually perfect.

What would your life look like? Are you working? What type of work are you doing? What do you do all day? Who is in your life?

Now that you know what the end looks like, what can you do today to take the first step in that direction?

Let yourself keep writing without editing and second-guessing anything you write. Write whatever comes to your mind. Just write every thought, and do this for a reasonable amount of time, up to an hour or more if necessary. Don't stop until your mind feels empty.

The longer you do it, the more words you will purge from your mind. It is even helpful to meditate before doing this, or while you are doing it to have some calming music on in the background, or while sitting outside in nature where it's quiet. Really let your thoughts run wild!

Often little gold nuggets will be set free during this process, even embedded in a sentence about something different entirely. You never know what the subconscious mind will bring forth when you unlock the door!

It's important to remember a life purpose may not just mean a career or a job. You might decide that your life purpose is to be a good mother, or volunteer with those less fortunate, or anything else that doesn't involve getting paid. As long as you feel that you are fulfilled, that is all that matters.

But you should not stay at a job that drags you down; there is no use in living your purpose doing good in the world if you are going to be miserable for the other part of your day.

CHAPTER 15

Why Connecting to the Universe Is Important

Connecting to the Universe is necessary for spiritual health. Our soul is crying out to be connected to where it came from. This makes up half of what we are; we are humans, and we are also spiritual beings, fragments of the one consciousness of the Universe.

Just like we have disconnected from nature, we have also disconnected from the Universe. This is what causes all of us to feel alone, lost, confused, scared, angry, depressed, separated, just about any negative feeling you can think of.

We are not alone, we are not separated from anything, but this disconnect creates the illusion that we are.

As above, so below. As within, so without. Everything that exists in the Universe exists in us and vice versa. We're all part of a big hydrogen, helium & oxygen soup! We cannot escape this connection, but we barely even recognize it is there. When we become disconnected from life, we become depressed.

Most people have, at some point in their lives, become depressed. Have you ever felt that you weren't good enough or that no one could love you, and you are utterly alone, so you feel there's no hope in going on?

Have you ever known someone who has felt this way? You might feel like nothing anyone can say would make you feel better. You might not know what to say to a person who is feeling this way.

Surely the depressed person has ran through every thought like "What is the purpose of my life?" or "Why am I even alive?" Usually, a person doesn't know the answers to those questions and therefore assumes if there is no clear answer, the Universe must not need them. If they feel there is no purpose, they feel the Universe has given up on them. But it hasn't.

Who is on your side from the moment you are born till the moment you die? The answer is not your parents. If you are depressed, you might feel like you yourself aren't good enough to have on your side, you want a higher power or even just an equal power that has your back and wants you to stick around.

Parents are usually gone by the time we reach the end of our life, and sometimes even if they are alive, we could have an estranged relationship with them. No matter what happens in life, who has your back?

The answer might surprise you; it's our cells! At the most microscopic level of your body, your cells' main job is to cooperate with the other cells and keep some part of you alive.

Your heart cells have one job; keep your heart beating and healthy. Same with every part of your body.

Now, in nature, you wouldn't expect one of those cells in one part of your body to just stop, right? It would go against nature for it to decide its job is too hard, and it isn't happy, and it wants to abandon the project. They fight to the death for your body to stay alive. They've got your back as long as they are able.

What a miracle it is that all the billions of cells in your body are in it for life. Next time you feel alone like nobody cares if you live or die, remember, your cells do. They're working around the clock to keep you alive.

This is why it is so important to feed your cells the right food. There are only two causes of disease: deficiency and toxicity. If your cells aren't getting the right nutrients, deficiency results in cell malfunction. If toxicity gets to the cell, it also results in cell malfunction. We must keep the proper nourishment going in, and we must keep the toxins out as much as possible.

The theme "as above so below" is a recurring one in our Universe. From the far reaches of the universe to the microscopic cells that make up every living thing on Earth, everything is a near-exact replica of everything else. It's like a fractal, the further in you go, you see it's just a smaller version of what you just went through.

It's also like a hologram, cut part of it out, and in that image, you see an exact miniature replica of the bigger image. You may have heard the words 'microcosm' and 'macrocosm,' which mean 'oneself' and 'the universe.' Connecting to the Universe is essentially being aware that these are one and the same, like a drop of water in the ocean.

If you were floating around out in space and you looked down onto Earth, what does it appear to be? Most people would think it's just a hard sphere like a marble; you can't see life on it, so it's probably just a bunch of gasses and clouds.

But then you get closer and start to see more details, pretty soon you see movement, and discover there are living things on this planet! Then you think ok, so that is what lives on this planet, people and animals.

But when you look closer at the people and animals, you would see all the cells & micro-organisms that make up the people and animals!

Think of it from your cells' perspective. The cells of your body work together as a whole; they form communities to keep each part of your body functioning.

All they know is 'we have to keep her heart beating' or 'we have to keep his liver filtering out impurities.' All this is happening at such a microscopic level comparable to what all living things are doing to the Earth.

You can't see us from space, just like you can't see our cells with the naked eye. And look at how vital your cells' ability to work together is necessary for the health and survival of their host, your body. Does this make you a little more conscious of our relationship with the Earth?

Meditation is probably the best way to feel your connection to the Universe. It is because meditation moves your awareness away from your body and allows space for your soul or higher self to speak to you. They say praying is how you talk to God, and meditating is how you listen.

I use the word "God" loosely; it can mean whatever you feel according to your beliefs. Empty space is necessary, disconnecting from everyday life is necessary, in order to tune in to the Universe and what your soul is telling you.

Related to meditation is writing. Writing is another excellent method of strengthening your connection to the Universe. The more you get your thoughts out of your head, the more space you have to be receptive to messages from the Universe. And the more you are grateful for, the more things you will find to be grateful for.

Whatever you focus on will grow, so it is essential to focus on the thoughts you want to manifest. This is the Law of Attraction. It isn't complicated like many people make it out to be. It's really a mind thing. Your thoughts become your reality once you see the opportunities that arise and take action on them. Let the Universe work it's magic, and you will feel a connection like never before!

Some people have a hard time connecting the Universe because they can't see it, as a whole. People tend to look up to the skies when talking about the Universe. It is humbling to look to the sky, especially at night, so we can get a feel for how small humans really are, and how much is out there. This is why nighttime sky gazing is such a common activity for humans.

However, the Universe is everywhere. So, while sky gazing is an excellent place to start, we won't figure out the meaning of life just by looking at the stars. There is a reason why ancient knowledge always tells us to look within. The answer is never out there; it is always inside.

Conclusion

I would like to thank you for taking the time to read this book! It is my sincere hope that you find yourself closer and closer every day to living a holistic lifestyle and that you can fully actualize the best version of yourself you can be!

Each subject I have discussed can be explored much more in-depth if you so choose. It was only my intent to introduce you to the foundations of a holistic lifestyle and to spark a fire within you to start your holistic lifestyle journey. I will most likely write more in-depth books in the future, but for now, I feel it is my duty to pass along to you a list of resources that have helped me get to where I am today in my journey.

Recommended books:

Whole Detox; A 21-Day Personalized Program to Break Through Barriers In Every Area Of Your Life by Dr. Deanna Minich

Idiot's Guide to Ayurveda by Sahara Rose

The Way of Herbs; Complete, Easy to Use Information on Simple Herbal Remedies for Natural Health and Healing by Michael Tierra

Perfect Health; A Complete Mind Body Guide by Deepak Chopra, M.D.

You Can Heal Your Life by Louise Hay

Earthing by Clinton Ober, Stephen T Sinatra M.D., and Martin Zucker

Never Be Sick Again by Raymond Francis

The Biology of Belief; Unleashing the Power of Consciousness, Matter & Miracles by Bruce H. Lipton, Ph.D.

Power Up Your Brain; The Neuroscience of Enlightenment

Essential Living; A Guide to Having Happiness and Peace by Reclaiming Your Essential Self by Shelley Uram, M.D.

Everyday Enlightenment; The Twelve Pathways to Personal Growth by Dan Millman

The Life You Were Born to Live; A Guide to Finding Your Life Purpose by Dan Millman

The Inner Matrix; A Guide to Transforming Your Life and Awakening Your Soul by Joey Klein

The Seat of the Soul by Gary Zukav

Transcending the Levels of Consciousness; The Stairway to Enlightenment by David R. Hawkins, M.D, Ph.D.

The Soul Searchers Handbook; The Modern Girl's Guide to the New Age World by Emma Mildon

The Renaissance Soul; How to Make Your Passions Your Life by Margaret Lobenstine

The Power of Now; A Guide to Spiritual Enlightenment by Eckhart Tolle

How to Think Like Leonardo DaVinci; Seven Steps to Genius Every Day by Michael J. Gelb

Awakening to the Natural State by John Wheeler

Recommended online courses:

The Ultimate Life Purpose Course by Leo Gura at Actualized.org

Eat Right For Your Mind-Body Type (12 Week Program) by Sahara Rose at iamSaharaRose.com

Recommended websites:

BodyMindSpiritDirectory.org

American Holistic Health Association; ahha.org

About the Author

For the past 15 years, Michelle has immersed herself in learning about holistic health. Sharing her knowledge with the world was the next obvious step.

Her interest in eating healthy started long ago when Michelle was in her 20's.

Then about ten years ago, she took her first course called Introduction to Natural Health & Healing through a local community college. Since she is almost continually learning, she feels like all of life is her teacher. Books, documentaries, websites, real-life experience, online courses, even YouTube videos, have been a source of never-ending information for her.

Just a few of the amazing authors, teachers and public figures she has learned from include; Deepak Chopra, Dr. Vasant Lad, Dr. Andrew Weil, Wayne Dyer, Louise Hay, Eckhart Tolle, Dr. Robert Morse, Dr. John McDougall, Sahara Rose, Leo Gura, Dr. Bruce Lipton, and many more!

Other courses she has taken or are currently taking include Ayurveda Basis by Janet Perez, Leo Gura's Ultimate Life Purpose Course, the Master Herbalist Diploma Course and the Naturopath Diploma course through Centre of Excellence, the Holistic Health and Wellness Coaching Certificate Program by Louise Anne Maurice, and Eat Right For Your Mind-Body Type by Sahara Rose.

If you have gotten any benefit from this book, please consider leaving a review on Amazon! Reviews help a book be seen by more people and are greatly appreciated!

Other books by Michelle Stern available on Amazon;

Glass Full of Gratitude; A Journal for Beginners to Change Your Perspective

Want-To-Do Lists

Road Trip Planner & Journal

Made in the USA
Columbia, SC
08 May 2022

60132335R00063